Get organ-ised for Biology with CGP...

There's a lot to learn in GCSE Biology, that's for sure. Luckily, this CGP book explains all the facts, theory and practical skills you'll need — with practice questions on each page to test you on what you've learned.

How to access your free Online Edition

This book includes a free Online Edition to read on your PC, Mac or tablet.
To access it, just go to **cgpbooks.co.uk/extras** and enter this code...

0715 7047 4369 9833

By the way, this code only works for one person. If somebody else has used this book before you, they might have already claimed the Online Edition.

CGP — still the best! ☺

Our sole aim here at CGP is to produce the highest quality books —
carefully written, immaculately presented and dangerously close to being funny.

Then we work our socks off to get them out to you
— at the cheapest possible prices.

Contents

Published by CGP
From original material by Richard Parsons.

Editors: Ciara McGlade, Rachael Rogers, Hayley Thompson, Sean Walsh.
Contributor: Paddy Gannon

ISBN: 978 1 78294 561 1

With thanks to Susan Alexander and Chris McGarry for the proofreading.

With thanks to Ana Pungartnik for the copyright research.

Data used for graph showing the prevalence of nonalcoholic fatty liver disease against the prevalence of obesity on page 26 from The Epidemiology of Nonalcoholic Fatty Liver Disease: A Global Perspective, Mariana Lazo, M.D., M.Sc.; Jeanne M. Clark, M.D., M.P.H Semin Liver Dis. 2008;28(4):339-350.

Data used for graph showing the risk of cardiovascular events against LDL levels on page 26 from P.M. Ridker, et al. Comparison of C-reactive protein and low density lipoprotein cholesterol levels in the prediction of first cardiovascular events. NEJM 2002; 347: 1557-65.

With thanks to Science Photo Library for permission to reproduce the image on page 60.

Printed by Elanders Ltd, Newcastle upon Tyne.
Clipart from Corel®

Cells and Genetic Material

When someone first peered down a microscope at a slice of cork and drew the boxes they saw, little did they know that they'd seen the <u>building blocks</u> of <u>every organism on the planet</u>...

Organisms can be Made from Eukaryotic or Prokaryotic Cells

1) <u>All living things</u> are made of <u>cells</u>.

2) Cells can be either <u>eukaryotic</u> or <u>prokaryotic</u>. Eukaryotic cells are <u>complex</u> and include all <u>animal</u> and <u>plant</u> cells. Prokaryotic cells are <u>smaller</u> and <u>simpler</u>, e.g. bacterial cells.

3) Both types of cell contain <u>genetic material</u> in the form of the chemical <u>DNA</u> — this contains <u>instructions</u> that control the <u>activities</u> of the <u>cell</u>, and allows the whole organism to <u>develop</u> and <u>function</u> as it should.

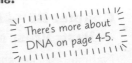
There's more about DNA on page 4-5.

4) Genetic material is <u>stored differently</u> in eukaryotic and prokaryotic cells (see below).

Eukaryotic Cells Have a Nucleus

Subcellular structures are also known as organelles.

The different parts of a cell are called <u>subcellular structures</u>. The diagram below shows a typical <u>animal cell</u>. Like most <u>eukaryotic</u> cells, it contains the following subcellular structures:

1) <u>Nucleus</u> — contains <u>genetic material</u>, which is arranged into <u>chromosomes</u> (see p.4).

2) <u>Cytoplasm</u> — gel-like substance where most of the <u>chemical reactions</u> happen. It contains <u>enzymes</u> (see page 32) that control these chemical reactions.

3) A <u>partially permeable cell membrane</u> — holds the cell together and controls what goes <u>in</u> and <u>out</u> (see page 37-38).

4) <u>Mitochondria</u> — contain the <u>enzymes</u> (see page 32) needed to control most of the reactions in aerobic <u>respiration</u>. Respiration transfers <u>energy</u> that the cell needs to work (see page 57).

5) <u>Ribosomes</u> — these are involved in the <u>synthesis of proteins</u> (see page 5).

Nucleus

Plant cells usually have <u>all the bits</u> that <u>animal</u> cells have, plus a few <u>extra</u> things that animal cells <u>don't</u> have:

1) Rigid <u>cell wall</u> — made of <u>cellulose</u>. It <u>supports</u> the cell and strengthens it.

2) <u>Large vacuole</u> — contains <u>cell sap</u>, a weak solution of sugar and salts.

3) <u>Chloroplasts</u> — these are where <u>photosynthesis</u> occurs, which makes food for the plant (see page 34). They contain a <u>green</u> substance called <u>chlorophyll</u>.

Prokaryotic Cells Have No Nucleus

1) <u>Prokaryotic cells</u> (such as bacteria) <u>don't have a nucleus</u>. Instead they store their <u>genetic material</u> as:

- <u>One</u> long <u>circular chromosome</u>, which <u>floats free</u> in the <u>cytoplasm</u>.

- <u>Plasmids</u> — <u>small loops</u> of <u>extra DNA</u>. They contain genes for things like <u>drug resistance</u>, and can be <u>passed</u> between prokaryotic cells. Not all prokaryotic cells contain plasmids.

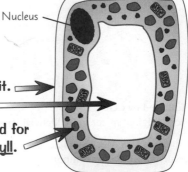

Cell membrane   Cell wall   Ribosomes

2) Prokaryotes also have other <u>subcellular structures</u>, such as:

3) Unlike eukaryotic cells, prokaryotic cells <u>don't</u> contain <u>mitochondria</u> or <u>chloroplasts</u>.

Cell structures — become a property developer...

The main difference between eukaryotic and prokaryotic cells is that eukaryotic cells contain a nucleus and prokaryotic cells don't. Both types of cell contain subcellular structures though, which each have their own function.

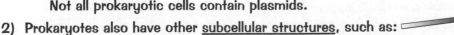

Q1   Give two ways in which genetic information may be stored in a prokaryotic cell.   [2 marks]

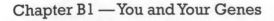

Cells and Microscopes

Without <u>microscopes</u> we would never have discovered cells. We can even use them to look <u>inside</u> cells.

You Need to Know How to View Cells Using a Light Microscope

Microscopes <u>magnify</u> images (make them look bigger) and allow things to be seen in more detail. <u>Light</u> <u>microscopes</u> work by passing <u>light</u> through the specimen (the sample you're looking at). They let you see subcellular structures, like <u>nuclei</u> and <u>chloroplasts</u>. This is how you'd use a light microscope to view cells:

1) Your specimen needs to <u>let light through it</u> so if your specimen is quite thick, you'll need to take a <u>thin slice</u> of it to start with.

2) Next, take a clean <u>slide</u> (a strip of clear glass or plastic) and use a <u>pipette</u> to put one drop of water or <u>mountant</u> (a clear, gloopy liquid) in the middle of it — this will <u>secure</u> the specimen in place.

3) Use <u>tweezers</u> to place your specimen on the slide.

4) Add a drop of <u>stain</u> if your <u>specimen</u> is completely <u>transparent</u> or <u>colourless</u> — this will make the specimen <u>easier to see</u>. <u>Different</u> stains are used to <u>highlight</u> different <u>structures</u>. For example, <u>eosin</u> is used to stain <u>cytoplasm</u> and <u>methylene blue</u> stains <u>DNA</u>.

5) Place a <u>cover slip</u> (a square of thin, transparent plastic or glass) at one end of the specimen, holding it at an <u>angle</u> with a <u>mounted needle</u>.

6) Carefully <u>lower</u> the cover slip onto the slide. Press it down <u>gently</u> with the <u>needle</u> so that no <u>air bubbles</u> are trapped under it.

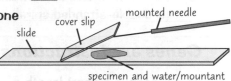

7) Clip the <u>prepared slide</u> onto the <u>stage</u> of the microscope.

8) Select the <u>lowest-powered objective lens</u> (i.e. the one that produces the lowest magnification).

9) Use the <u>coarse adjustment knob</u> to move the stage <u>up</u> so that the slide is <u>just underneath</u> the objective lens. Then, <u>looking</u> down the <u>eyepiece</u>, move the stage <u>downwards</u> (so you don't accidently crash it into the lens) until the specimen is <u>nearly in focus</u>.

10) Then <u>adjust the focus</u> with the <u>fine adjustment knob</u>, until you get a <u>clear image</u>.

11) If you need to see your specimen with <u>greater magnification</u>, swap to a <u>higher-powered objective lens</u> and <u>refocus</u>.

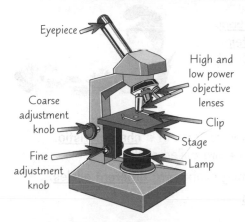

You Might Need to Produce a Scientific Drawing of a Specimen

1) You should draw what you see under the microscope using a <u>pencil</u> with a <u>sharp point</u>.

2) Make sure your drawing takes up <u>at least half</u> of the space available and that it is drawn with <u>clear, unbroken lines</u>.

3) Your drawing should not include any <u>colouring</u> or <u>shading</u>.

4) If you are drawing <u>cells</u>, the <u>subcellular structures</u> should be drawn in <u>proportion</u>.

5) Remember to include a <u>title</u> of what you were observing and write down the <u>magnification</u> that it was observed under.

6) You should also <u>label</u> the <u>important features</u> of your drawing (e.g. nucleus, chloroplasts), using <u>straight lines</u> drawn with a <u>ruler</u>. Make sure that none of these lines <u>cross each other</u> because this can make them hard to read.

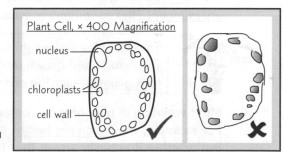

Plant Cell, × 400 Magnification

What, no colouring pencils? Scientists are spoilsports...

There's lots of important stuff here about how you use a light microscope to view specimens — so get learning.

Q1 A student prepares a slide with a sample of onion cells and places it on the stage of a light microscope. Describe the steps she should take to get a focused image of the cells. [4 marks]

Genomes and Characteristics

Right, time to find out exactly what this genetic material is all about and why it's so blummin' important...

Chromosomes are Really Long Molecules of DNA

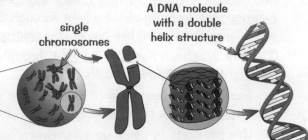

A DNA molecule with a double helix structure

single chromosomes

1) The genome is the entire genetic material of an organism.

2) In plant and animal cells, genetic material is stored in the nucleus and is arranged into chromosomes.

3) The chromosomes normally come in pairs — e.g. humans have 23 pairs (so 46 chromosomes in total).

4) Each chromosome is one very long molecule of DNA that's coiled up.

5) DNA is a polymer — a molecule that's made up of smaller, repeating units called monomers. DNA is made from monomers called nucleotides. There's more on these on the next page.

6) Each DNA molecule contains two strands of nucleotides, which coil together to form a double helix (a double-stranded spiral).

Genes are Instructions in the Genome

1) A gene is a short length of DNA on a chromosome.

2) Each gene codes for (tells the cells to make) a particular sequence of amino acids, which are put together to make a specific protein. This process of making a big molecule (e.g. a protein) from lots of smaller molecules (e.g. amino acids) is called polymerisation.

3) Proteins control the development of different characteristics, e.g. dimples, and how an organism functions.

4) Genes can exist in different versions. Each version gives a different form of a characteristic, like blue or brown eyes. The different versions of the same gene are called alleles.

5) Each chromosome in a pair carries the same genes, but they may each carry different alleles.

6) Different versions of a gene can also be called genetic variants.

Genes and the Environment can Influence Characteristics

1) The combination of alleles an organism has for each gene is called its genotype. An organism's genotype is what makes its genome unique.

2) The characteristics the organism displays is called its phenotype.

3) It's not only genotype that can affect an organism's phenotype — interactions with the environment (the conditions in which the organisms lives) can modify a phenotype.

For example, a plant grown on a nice sunny windowsill could grow luscious and green. The same plant grown in darkness would grow tall and spindly and its leaves would turn yellow — so the characteristics it displays would be affected by its environment.

4) Most variation in phenotype is determined by a mixture of genetic and environmental factors. For example, the maximum height that an animal or plant could grow to is determined by its genes. But whether it actually grows that tall depends on its environment (e.g. how much food it gets).

Insert joke about genes and jeans here...

There are so many, I thought you could come up with your own as a bit of light relief. Make sure that you're clued up on this stuff about genomes, DNA, genes, genotypes and phenotypes before you move on.

Q1   What is an organism's genome?   [1 mark]

Q2   What is an organism's: a) genotype,   b) phenotype?   [2 marks]

DNA and Protein Synthesis

So here's how life works — DNA molecules contain a <u>code</u> that determines which <u>proteins</u> are built.

DNA is Made Up of Nucleotides

1) As you saw on the previous page, DNA is a <u>polymer</u> made from <u>nucleotides</u>. There are <u>four</u> different nucleotides in DNA.

2) Each nucleotide consists of one <u>sugar molecule</u>, one <u>phosphate group</u> and one '<u>base</u>'. The <u>sugar</u> and <u>phosphate</u> molecules are <u>common</u> to all DNA nucleotides (i.e. they're the same in all DNA nucleotides) but the <u>base varies</u>.

3) The sugar and phosphate molecules in the nucleotides form a '<u>backbone</u>' to the DNA strands. A base <u>joins</u> to each <u>sugar</u>.

4) The four different bases found in a DNA molecule are: <u>adenine (A)</u>, <u>thymine (T)</u>, <u>cytosine (C)</u> and <u>guanine (G)</u>.

5) Each base <u>links</u> to a base on the opposite strand in the helix.

6) <u>A</u> always pairs up with <u>T</u>, and <u>C</u> always pairs up with <u>G</u>. This is called <u>complementary base pairing</u>.

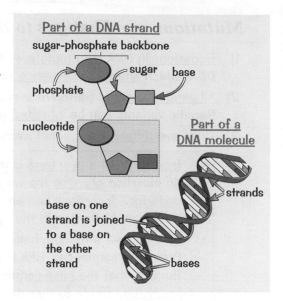

Part of a DNA strand

sugar-phosphate backbone

phosphate — sugar — base

nucleotide

Part of a DNA molecule

base on one strand is joined to a base on the other strand

strands

bases

Proteins are Polymers Made Up of Amino Acids

1) It's the <u>order</u> of <u>bases</u> in a <u>gene</u> that decides the order of <u>amino acids</u> in a <u>protein</u>.

2) Each amino acid is <u>coded for</u> by a sequence of <u>three bases</u> in the gene called a <u>triplet</u>. For example, the triplet <u>AGG</u> codes for the amino acid <u>arginine</u>. The sequence <u>AGGCTT</u> codes for <u>arginine</u>, then <u>leucine</u>.

3) The amino acids are <u>joined together</u> to make various proteins, depending on the <u>order</u> of <u>bases</u> in the gene. The <u>properties</u> of each <u>protein</u> are determined by the particular <u>amino acids</u> it contains and the <u>order</u> they're present in.

The order of bases in all of an organism's DNA (genome) is called its genetic code.

Using letters to represent the bases in DNA is an example of a model — see p.99 for more.

Proteins are Synthesised in the Cytoplasm

1) <u>DNA</u> is found in the cell <u>nucleus</u> and can't move out of it because it's <u>really big</u>. The cell needs to get the information from the <u>DNA</u> to the cell <u>cytoplasm</u> where <u>proteins</u> are <u>synthesised</u>.

2) This is done using a molecule called <u>messenger RNA (mRNA)</u>. Like DNA, mRNA is a <u>polymer</u> of <u>nucleotides</u>, but it's <u>shorter</u> and only a <u>single strand</u>. mRNA also uses <u>uracil (U)</u> instead of <u>thymine (T)</u> as a <u>base</u>. Uracil (U) still pairs with <u>adenine (A)</u>.

3) This is how proteins are made:

1) The <u>DNA</u> contains the <u>gene</u> coding for the <u>protein</u>.

2) In the nucleus, the two DNA strands <u>unzip</u>. The DNA is used as a <u>template</u> to make the <u>mRNA</u>. <u>Base pairing</u> ensures the mRNA is <u>complementary</u> to the opposite DNA strand.

3) The <u>mRNA</u> molecule then moves <u>out of the nucleus</u> and <u>into the cytoplasm</u>, where it attaches to a <u>ribosome</u>.

4) <u>Amino acids</u> are then <u>joined together</u> in the correct order by the <u>ribosome</u>, following the order of the <u>triplets</u> in the mRNA. This makes the <u>protein</u> coded for by the gene.

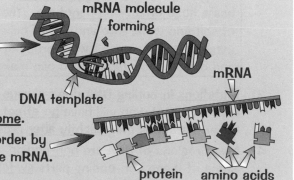

mRNA molecule forming

DNA template

mRNA

protein   amino acids

A triplet of bases — three-tiered cheesecake anyone...

Definitely been watching too much Bake Off. Remember — the order of bases in the DNA is copied to create mRNA, which moves to the cytoplasm. Then a chain of amino acids is built up according to the order of the bases.

Q1   Explain how a gene codes for a protein.   [2 marks]

Mutations and Genetic Variants

Sometimes the <u>sequence</u> of <u>DNA bases</u> can be changed. These changes are called <u>mutations</u>. Read on...

Mutations are Changes to the Genome

1) <u>Occasionally</u> DNA may <u>mutate</u> — this means a <u>random change</u> occurs in the DNA, which <u>alters</u> the <u>sequence of bases</u> within the molecule.

> Alleles (see next page) are genetic variants.

2) <u>All genetic variants</u> (different versions of genes) are formed by <u>mutations</u>. Genetic variants can be <u>inherited</u> (passed down from a parent to its offspring).

3) There are <u>different ways</u> that mutations can change the DNA base sequence. For example:

- <u>Insertions</u> — a <u>new base</u> is <u>inserted</u> into the DNA base sequence where it shouldn't be. An insertion <u>changes</u> the way the <u>triplets</u> are '<u>read</u>', which can change the <u>amino acids</u> they code for. Insertions can change <u>more than one</u> amino acid as they have a <u>knock-on effect</u> on the bases further on in the sequence.

- <u>Deletions</u> — a random base is <u>deleted</u> from the DNA base sequence. Like insertions, they <u>change</u> the way that the <u>base sequence</u> is '<u>read</u>' and have <u>knock-on effects</u> further down the sequence.

Original gene — T A T A G T C T T
Amino acid coded for — Tyrosine Serine Leucine

insertion here

Mutated gene — T A T A G G T C T T
Amino acid coded for — Tyrosine Arginine Serine

- <u>Substitutions</u> — a random base in the DNA base sequence is <u>changed</u> to a different base. Some amino acids are coded for by <u>more than one triplet</u>, so substitution mutations <u>don't always change</u> the <u>amino acids</u> in a protein. E.g. the amino acid tyrosine is coded for by **TAT** <u>and</u> **TAC**.

> You don't need to learn what amino acid each triplet codes for, or the names of any amino acids.

Mutations can Affect the Proteins an Organism Makes

1) If a <u>mutation</u> leads to a change in the amino acid sequence coded for by a gene, this could change the <u>structure</u> and <u>function</u> of the <u>final protein</u> — the protein might work differently or it may stop working altogether. For example:

> <u>Enzymes</u> are <u>proteins</u> that speed up chemical reactions in an organism (see p.32). They have to have a very <u>specific shape</u> to be able to work properly. A <u>mutation</u> in a gene that codes for an enzyme might result in the enzyme's shape <u>changing</u> so much that it's no longer be able to perform its function.

2) A change in the function of a <u>single protein</u> occasionally has a <u>big effect</u> on <u>phenotype</u> (characteristics). For example:

> The genetic disorder, <u>cystic fibrosis</u>, can be caused by the <u>deletion</u> of <u>just three bases</u> but it has a <u>huge effect</u> on <u>phenotype</u>. The gene codes for a <u>protein</u> that controls the <u>movement</u> of salt and water into and out of cells. However, the protein produced by the <u>cystic fibrosis genetic variant</u> doesn't work properly. This leads to <u>excess mucus production</u> in the lungs and digestive system, which can make it difficult to breathe and to digest food.

3) <u>Mutations</u> in coding DNA <u>don't always change</u> the <u>amino acid sequence</u> of a protein though — in these cases the mutation will have <u>no effect</u> on protein structure or function and <u>no effect</u> on <u>phenotype</u>. Other mutations only <u>slightly alter</u> protein function and lead to a very <u>small effect</u> on phenotype.

4) Many regions of DNA are <u>non-coding</u> — this means that they don't code for any amino acids. Some of these non-coding parts <u>switch genes on and off</u>, so they <u>control</u> whether or not a gene is <u>expressed</u> (used to make a protein). Mutations in non-coding DNA may <u>prevent</u> a protein from being <u>produced</u>, which may in turn affect the organism's <u>phenotype</u>.

I was hoping for the 'grow wings' mutation — I'm still waiting...

Mutations might sound alarming, but actually most are tiny changes that don't affect the phenotype at all.

Q1   Explain why a gene mutation may affect the phenotype of an organism.   [3 marks]

Genetic Diagrams

This page is about how <u>characteristics</u> are <u>inherited</u> — it involves drawing little <u>diagrams</u> too, which is (a bit) fun.

Alleles are Different Versions of the Same Gene

1) In <u>sexual reproduction</u>, the mother and father produce <u>gametes</u> (reproductive cells), e.g. <u>sperm</u> and <u>eggs</u>. Each gamete only has <u>one copy</u> of <u>each chromosome</u> (rather than having pairs of chromosomes like other cells — see p.4). So gametes only have <u>one version of each gene</u> (i.e. <u>one allele</u>).

2) To produce an offspring, the chromosomes from a <u>male gamete</u> get <u>mixed together</u> with those from a <u>female gamete</u> — so the offspring ends up with <u>pairs of chromosomes</u> and <u>two alleles</u> for each gene.

3) If the alleles are <u>different</u>, then the organism has <u>instructions</u> for <u>two different versions</u> of a characteristic (e.g. freckles or no freckles) but it only <u>shows one version</u> of the two (e.g. freckles). The version of the characteristic that appears is caused by the <u>dominant allele</u>. The other allele is said to be <u>recessive</u>. The characteristic caused by the recessive allele only appears if <u>both alleles</u> are recessive.

4) In genetic diagrams, <u>letters</u> are used to represent <u>genes</u>. Dominant alleles are always shown with a <u>capital letter</u> (e.g. 'C') and <u>recessive alleles</u> with a <u>small letter</u> (e.g. 'c').

5) If you're <u>homozygous</u> for a trait, you have <u>two alleles the same</u> for that particular gene, e.g. <u>CC</u> or <u>cc</u>. If you're <u>heterozygous</u> for a trait, you have <u>two different alleles</u> for that particular gene, e.g. <u>Cc</u>.

6) Remember, an organism's <u>genotype</u> is the alleles it has. Its <u>phenotype</u> is the characteristics it displays.

Genetic Diagrams show the Possible Alleles in the Offspring

Some characteristics are controlled by a <u>single gene</u>, e.g. blood group — this is called <u>single gene inheritance</u>. Genetic diagrams help to <u>predict the phenotype</u> of the <u>offspring</u> when you know the <u>genotype</u> of the <u>parents</u>.

Let's say an allele that causes hamsters to have superpowers is <u>recessive</u> ("b"), and that <u>normal</u> (boring) hamsters don't have superpowers due to a <u>dominant</u> allele ("B").

1) A hamster with superpowers <u>must</u> have the <u>genotype bb</u> (i.e. it must be homozygous for this trait).

2) However, a <u>boring hamster</u> could have <u>two</u> possible genotypes — BB (homozygous) or Bb (heterozygous), because the dominant allele (B) <u>overrules</u> the recessive one (b).

3) Here's what happens if you breed from two <u>heterozygous</u> hamsters:

Parents' <u>phenotypes</u>:	boring	boring
Parents' <u>genotypes</u>:	Bb	Bb
Gametes' <u>genotypes</u>:	B b	B b
Offsprings' <u>genotypes</u>:	BB Bb Bb bb	
Offsprings' <u>phenotypes</u>:	boring boring boring <u>superpowered!</u>	

There's a <u>75% chance</u> of having a boring hamster, and a <u>25% chance</u> of one with superpowers. To put that another way... you'd expect a <u>3:1 ratio</u> of boring:superpowered hamsters. Or yet another way... out of 100 hamsters, the <u>proportion</u> of them you'd expect to have superpowers would be 25.

4) If you breed <u>two homozygous</u> hamsters there's only <u>one possible offspring</u> you can end up with. E.g. breeding BB and bb hamsters can only give offspring with a <u>Bb</u> genotype — and they'd all have a <u>boring</u> phenotype.

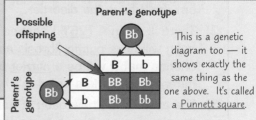

This is a genetic diagram too — it shows exactly the same thing as the one above. It's called a <u>Punnett square</u>.

However, it's not always quite this simple — <u>most</u> characteristics are actually controlled by <u>multiple genes</u>. (You don't need to be able to draw the genetic diagrams for these though.)

Your meanotype determines how nice you are to your sibling...

Remember, results like this are only probabilities. It doesn't mean it <u>will</u> happen.

Q1   The height of garden pea plants is controlled by a single gene with two alleles. The allele for tall plants (T) is dominant over the allele for dwarf plants (t). Two heterozygous pea plants are crossed. Draw a genetic diagram to find what proportion of the offspring would be expected to be dwarf plants.   [3 marks]

More Genetic Diagrams

Here's <u>another</u> page of funny diagrams with squares, circles and lines going everywhere. And it's not the last...

Your Chromosomes Control Whether You're Male or Female

1) There are <u>23 pairs</u> of <u>chromosomes</u> in every human body cell. The <u>23rd pair</u> are labelled <u>XY</u> or <u>XX</u>. These are <u>sex chromosomes</u> — they decide whether you turn out <u>male</u> or <u>female</u>.

   - <u>Males</u> have an <u>X</u> and a <u>Y</u> chromosome: XY
   - <u>Females</u> have <u>two X chromosomes</u>:   XX

2) Like other characteristics, sex is determined by <u>genes</u>.

3) The <u>Y chromosome</u> carries a gene which makes an embryo develop into a <u>male</u> as it grows, by stimulating the growth of <u>testes</u>. <u>Females</u>, who don't have a Y chromosome, don't have this gene and so they develop in a different way.

4) The <u>genetic diagram</u> for sex inheritance is fairly similar to a bog-standard one. It just shows the <u>sex chromosomes</u> rather than different alleles.

5) Sometimes, you might see a genetic diagram showing the <u>inheritance</u> of an <u>allele</u> on one of the <u>sex chromosomes</u>. The sex chromosome and the allele can be shown together like this: X^H or X^h.

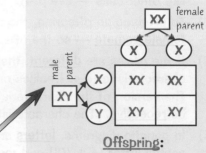

<u>Offspring</u>:

Two XX genotypes and <u>two XY</u> genotypes, so there's a <u>50% chance</u> of having either a <u>boy</u> or a <u>girl</u>. This means there is a <u>50:50 ratio</u> of boys to girls.

Family Trees Can Also Show Single Gene Inheritance

Knowing how inheritance works helps you to interpret a different type of genetic diagram called a <u>family tree</u>. Here's a worked example using <u>cystic fibrosis</u> — a genetic disorder of the cell membranes.

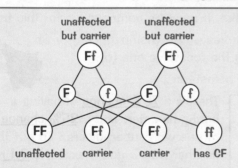

unaffected but carrier   unaffected but carrier

unaffected   carrier   carrier   has CF

1) The allele which causes cystic fibrosis (CF) is a <u>recessive allele</u>, 'f', carried by about <u>1 person in 30</u>.

2) Because it's recessive, people with only <u>one copy</u> of the allele <u>won't</u> have the disorder — they're known as <u>carriers</u>.

3) For a child to have a chance of inheriting the disorder, <u>both parents</u> must either have the disorder themselves or be <u>carriers</u>.

4) As the diagram shows, there's a <u>1 in 4 chance</u> of a child having the disorder if <u>both</u> parents are <u>carriers</u>.

Below is a <u>family tree</u> for a family that includes <u>carriers</u> of <u>cystic fibrosis</u>. The lines on the family tree link the parents to each other (horizontal) and to their children (vertical).

1) You can see from the family tree that the <u>allele</u> for cystic fibrosis <u>isn't</u> dominant because plenty of the family <u>carry</u> the allele but don't have the disorder.

2) There is a 1 in 4 (<u>25%</u>) chance that the new baby will have <u>cystic fibrosis</u> and a 1 in 2 (<u>50%</u>) chance that it will be a <u>carrier</u> because <u>both</u> of its parents are carriers but don't have the disorder.

3) The case of the new baby is just the same as in the genetic diagram above — so the baby could be <u>unaffected</u> (FF), a <u>carrier</u> (Ff) or have the <u>disorder</u> (ff).

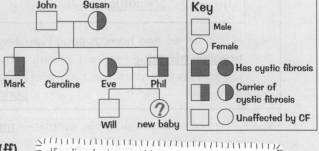

John   Susan

Mark   Caroline   Eve   Phil

Will   new baby

Key

☐ Male

◯ Female

■ ● Has cystic fibrosis

◫ ◖ Carrier of cystic fibrosis

☐ ◯ Unaffected by CF

If a disorder is caused by a dominant allele, there will be no carriers shown on the family tree.

Have you got the Y-factor...

I bet you're sick of genetic diagrams by now. Still, that family tree makes a nice change. Umm... sort of.

Q1   Use the family tree above for the following question. Mark and his wife (who is not shown in the diagram) have a baby with cystic fibrosis. What are the possible genotypes of Mark's wife?   [1 mark]

Mendel

Some people forget about Mendel but I reckon he's the <u>Granddaddy of Genetics</u>. His work helped scientists to understand all the clever stuff they know about <u>genes</u> and <u>alleles</u> today.

Mendel Helped Us Understand Genetics

<u>Gregor Mendel</u> was an Austrian monk. On his garden plot, he noted how <u>characteristics</u> in <u>plants</u> were <u>passed on</u> from one generation to the next. The results of his research were published in <u>1866</u> and eventually became the <u>foundation</u> of modern <u>genetics</u>. He carried out crosses for <u>height</u> in <u>pea plants</u>:

1) Mendel crossed a <u>tall</u> pea plant with a <u>dwarf</u> pea plant. <u>All</u> the offspring were <u>tall</u>.

2) So, Mendel took two of the <u>tall</u> plants from the <u>first</u> set of offspring and crossed them. This time, <u>75%</u> of the offspring were <u>tall</u> but <u>25%</u> were <u>dwarf</u> plants.

3) This is explained nicely by a <u>genetic diagram</u>:

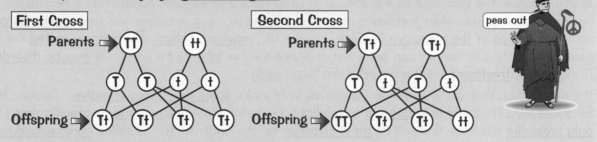

| First Cross | Second Cross | peas out |

4) Mendel realised that the height characteristic in pea plants was determined by separate "<u>inherited factors</u>" passed on from each parent. The ratios of tall and dwarf plants in the offspring showed that the factor for tall plants, <u>T</u>, was <u>dominant</u> over the factor for dwarf plants, <u>t</u>.

This is an example of a scientist coming up with an explanation for data he or she has collected.

Our Understanding of Genetics Has Advanced Greatly Since Mendel's Work

1) We now know that Mendel's "inherited factors" are of course <u>genes</u>. We also know that, unlike height in pea plants, <u>most characteristics</u> are <u>determined</u> by the <u>interactions</u> of <u>multiple genes</u> in <u>different parts</u> of the <u>genome</u>. But back in Mendel's day <u>nobody</u> knew anything about DNA or genes.

2) It wasn't until a long time after his death that other scientists linked his inherited factors with genes and chromosomes — and realised the <u>significance</u> of his work.

3) <u>Now</u>, the study of <u>genetics</u> has <u>advanced</u> so much that scientists are even able to find out the <u>order of nucleotides</u> in an organism's <u>genome</u> — this is called <u>genome sequencing</u>.

4) Scientists can use genome sequencing to identify <u>which parts</u> of the genome <u>control different characteristics</u>. Since most characteristics are controlled <u>by more than one gene</u>, this isn't an easy task:

> For example, our <u>height</u> is influenced by <u>DNA sequences</u> in <u>over 400 locations</u> within our genome. <u>Genetic variants</u> in these locations <u>interact</u> with each other to determine how tall we will be.

Remember, environmental factors also influence characteristics such as height (see page 4).

5) Once scientists have <u>worked out</u> which <u>genetic variants</u> influence different characteristics in an organism, they can use the information for a <u>range of purposes</u>. For example:

- To <u>test</u> whether people are susceptible to <u>diseases</u> that are influenced by genetic variants (see next page).
- To <u>modify organisms</u> so they contain a <u>specific gene</u> (see page 11).

Clearly, being a monk in the 1800s was a right laugh...

Well, there was no TV in those days, you see. Monks had to make their own entertainment. And in Mendel's case, that involved growing lots and lots of peas. He was a very clever lad, was Mendel, but unfortunately just a bit ahead of his time. Nobody had a clue what he was going on about.

Q1   Explain how Mendel contributed to modern-day understanding of genetic inheritance.   [3 marks]

Genome Research and Testing

Scientists might be able to use genes to predict diseases and provide us with new and better drugs. Cool innit?

Scientists Have Researched the Human Genome

Scientists have identified all of the genes found in the human genome. This has lots of potential uses in medicine — by comparing the genomes of people with and without a certain disease, scientists can try to identify the genetic variants that are involved in the disease. People can then be tested for the genetic variants that are linked to a particular disease.

Genetic Testing Can Help To Improve Healthcare

1) Some genetic variants put you at a higher risk of developing a certain disease, e.g. some types of cancer. If people knew they had a particular variant, they may be able to make lifestyle changes to reduce this risk.

2) In some cases, the presence of a particular genetic variant or variants means that a person will definitely have a disease (rather than just being more likely to get it). E.g. a person will have cystic fibrosis if they have two copies of the recessive CF allele. In the UK, newborn babies are routinely tested for certain genetic variants, so doctors can tell whether or not they've inherited a particular genetic disorder. If they have, treatment for the disorder can begin early.

3) It's now known that some common genetic variants make some drugs less effective. Genetic testing for these variants could help doctors to predict how their patient will respond to specific drugs and only prescribe the ones that will be most effective for the patient. This is called personalised medicine.

There are drawbacks with this kind of genetic testing though. For example, it could lead to:

1) Discrimination — employers may discriminate against people who are genetically likely to get a disease.
2) Increased stress — if people knew they were susceptible to a nasty brain disease, they could panic every time they get a headache (even if they never get the disease).

Genetic Testing May Also Help People With Family Planning

A couple wanting to have a baby could use genetic testing to identify the risk of their baby having a particular genetic disorder. This could involve testing of the parents and of the embryo or fetus.

1) Parent — one of the parents may know there is a genetic disorder within their family. Even though they may not have the disorder, genetic tests could reveal whether they are a carrier for the condition.

2) Embryo — a couple who know they are at risk of passing on a genetic disorder may choose to have their eggs fertilised in a lab. A cell can be taken from each resulting embryo and its DNA analysed. An embryo without the genetic variants linked to the disorder can be implanted into the womb to develop into a baby.

3) Fetus — once a woman is pregnant, it is possible to get some of the fetal DNA by taking a sample of the amniotic fluid, which surrounds the fetus in the womb. (This procedure carries a very small risk of miscarriage.) The fetal DNA can then be tested for the genetic variants linked to the disorder. If the test is positive the couple can decide whether they wish to continue with the pregnancy.

This kind of genetic testing allows couples to make informed decisions about family planning. But...

1) Testing isn't 100% perfect. E.g. a couple could receive a positive test result during pregnancy (suggesting that their unborn baby will have a genetic disorder) but the test result may be wrong, causing the couple unnecessary stress. Alternatively, a couple who incorrectly receive a negative test result may not be prepared for coping with their child's disorder when he or she is born.

2) Genetic testing can lead to the destruction of embryos or a termination. Some people think that any potential life should be allowed to survive, whatever disorders he or she may have. There's also a worry that genetic testing is a 'slippery slope' and that there may come a point where everyone wants to screen their embryos and pick the most 'desirable' one, e.g. they may want a blonde, blue-eyed boy.

Personalised medicine — writing your name on a pill...

Pfft... nothing's ever straight-forward is it. Make sure you know the pros and cons of using genetic testing.

Q1   Describe a test that could be carried out to determine whether a fetus has a genetic disorder.   [2 marks]

Genetic Engineering

Genetic engineering is an interesting area of science with <u>exciting possibilities</u>, but there might be <u>dangers</u> too...

Genetic Engineering Transfers Genes Between Organisms

The basic idea of genetic engineering is to <u>transfer</u> a <u>gene</u> from the <u>genome</u> of one organism to the genome of <u>another</u>. This gives the organism that receives the gene <u>new</u> and <u>useful characteristics</u>. For example:

- The <u>gene</u> for the <u>human insulin</u> protein has been inserted into <u>bacteria</u>. The bacteria are grown in large numbers to produce insulin for the <u>treatment</u> of <u>diabetes</u>.
- A <u>gene</u> that helps <u>fish</u> to survive in <u>cold water</u> has been inserted into <u>tomato plants</u> to help the plants <u>survive</u> at <u>low temperatures</u>.

Genetic engineering works because all organisms use the same molecule (DNA) to store their genetic material.

Here's how it works:

1) A useful gene is <u>isolated</u> (cut) from an organism's genome using <u>enzymes</u>. The gene is then <u>replicated</u> to produce lots of copies.

2) Each copy is then inserted into a <u>vector</u>. The vector is usually a <u>virus</u> or a <u>bacterial plasmid</u> (see page 2) depending on the type of organism that the gene is being transferred to.

3) The <u>vectors</u> are then <u>mixed with other cells</u>, e.g. bacteria. The idea is that the vectors (containing the desired gene) will be <u>taken up</u> by the cells, which will become <u>genetically modified</u>.

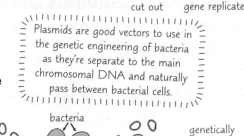

DNA — desired gene — gene cut out — gene replicated

Plasmids are good vectors to use in the genetic engineering of bacteria as they're separate to the main chromosomal DNA and naturally pass between bacterial cells.

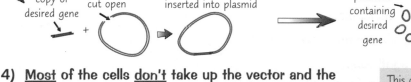

copy of desired gene + plasmid cut open → desired gene inserted into plasmid → plasmids containing desired gene + bacteria → genetically modified bacterium

4) <u>Most</u> of the cells <u>don't</u> take up the vector and the desired gene, so the cells that have been modified need to be <u>identified</u> and <u>selected</u>.

This can be done by adding a <u>marker gene</u> to the vectors, along with the desired gene. The marker gene allows cells that have taken up the vectors to be identified, e.g. some marker genes cause cells to <u>fluoresce</u> (glow) under UV light.

5) The <u>selected cells</u> are then allowed to <u>replicate</u> — each new cell will contain the <u>desired gene</u> and produce the <u>protein</u> it codes for.

Genetic Engineering is Useful in Agriculture and Medicine

1) For example, in <u>agriculture</u>, <u>crops</u> can be genetically modified to be <u>resistant to herbicides</u> (chemicals that kill plants). Making crops <u>herbicide-resistant</u> means farmers can <u>spray</u> their crops to <u>kill weeds</u>, <u>without</u> affecting the crop itself. This can <u>increase crop yield</u>, helping us to produce <u>more food</u> for the growing human population.

2) In <u>medicine</u>, genetically engineering <u>bacteria</u> to produce human <u>insulin</u> has helped to improve healthcare. Researchers have also managed to transfer <u>human genes</u> that produce <u>useful proteins</u> into <u>sheep</u> and <u>cows</u>, e.g. human <u>antibodies</u> used in therapy for illnesses like <u>arthritis</u>. These proteins can then be <u>extracted</u> from the animal, e.g. from their <u>milk</u>.

3) However, there are <u>concerns</u> about the genetic engineering of animals. It can be hard to predict what <u>effect</u> modifying its genome will have <u>on the organism</u> — many genetically modified embryos <u>don't survive</u> and some genetically modified <u>animals</u> suffer from <u>health problems</u> later in life.

4) There are also <u>concerns</u> about growing genetically modified crops. One is that <u>transplanted genes</u> may get out into the <u>environment</u>. E.g. a herbicide resistance gene may be picked up by <u>weeds</u>, creating a new 'superweed' variety. Another concern is that genetically modified crops could <u>adversely</u> affect <u>food chains</u> — or even <u>human health</u>. Some think that more <u>long-term studies</u> need to be carried out so the risks are more fully understood.

I say it's great.

If only there was a gene to make revision easier...

As with most new technologies there are benefits and risks to genetic engineering. Make sure you learn them.

Q1   Explain one benefit of being able to genetically engineer herbicide-resistant crops.   **[2 marks]**

Revision Questions for Chapter B1

Hooray! You're at the end of the Chapter B1 — by now you should understand just how important DNA is.
- Try these questions and <u>tick off each one</u> when you <u>get it right</u>.
- When you've done <u>all the questions</u> for a topic and are <u>completely happy</u> with it, tick off the topic.

Cells, Genetic Material and Microscopy (p.2-3) ☑

1) State whether each of the following is a eukaryotic cell or a prokaryotic cell:
   a) animal cell   b) bacterial cell   c) plant cell. ☑
2) True or false? All cells contain genetic material. ☑
3) Where is genetic material stored in a eukaryotic cell? ☑
4) Why is it necessary to use thin samples of tissue when viewing cells using a light microscope? ☑
5) Why are samples sometimes stained before viewing under a light microscope? ☑

DNA, Protein Synthesis and Genetic Variants (p.4-6) ☑

6) Why is DNA described as a polymer? ☑
7) What is a gene? ☑
8) What is an allele? ☑
9) What interacts with an organism's genotype to determine its phenotype? ☑
10) Draw a single nucleotide. ☑
11) Name the four different bases in a DNA molecule. ☑
12) How many bases in a DNA sequence code for one amino acid? ☑
13) Describe the role of mRNA in protein synthesis. ☑
14) Explain how a mutation leads to the formation of a genetic variant. ☑
15) How can a mutation in non-coding DNA affect the phenotype of an organism? ☑

Genetic Diagrams and Mendel (p.7-9) ☐

16) In a genetic diagram, is a capital letter used to represent a dominant or recessive allele? ☑
17) What does it mean if an organism is
    a) homozygous for a gene?
    b) heterozygous for a gene? ☑
18) What are the 23rd pair of chromosomes labelled as in a female? ☐
19) A couple have a child.
    What's the probability that the child will have the **XX** combination of sex chromosomes? ☑
20) How are carriers shown on a family tree? ☑
21) Describe the experiment that Mendel used to study the inheritance of height in pea plants. ☑
22) What does the term 'genome sequencing' mean? ☑

Genome Research and Genetic Engineering (p.10-11) ☑

23) How has research on the human genome led to the potential development of personalised medicines? ☑
24) Give one potential drawback of genetic testing in healthcare. ☑
25) What does 'genetic engineering' mean? ☑
26) Describe two concerns people may have about using genetic engineering in agriculture. ☑

Health and Disease

If you're feeling <u>bright-eyed</u> and <u>bushy-tailed</u> then you might not be for much <u>longer</u>. Here's a page on <u>diseases</u>.

Organisms' Health Can be Affected by Disease

1) A <u>healthy</u> organism is one that is in a state of <u>well-being</u>
   — it's <u>functioning</u> just as it <u>should</u> be, both <u>physically</u> and <u>mentally</u>.

2) A <u>disease</u> is a condition that commonly damages cells of the host and <u>impairs</u> the <u>normal structures</u>
   or <u>functioning</u> of the organism. Most organisms will experience disease <u>at some point</u> in their lifetime.

3) There are many <u>causes</u> of <u>disease</u> and <u>ill health</u>. For example:

   - the organism may become <u>infected</u> by a <u>pathogen</u> (see below).
   - there may be a <u>mutation</u> in the organism's <u>genes</u> (see page 6).
   - the organism may be affected by <u>environmental conditions</u>,
     e.g. if a plant <u>doesn't get enough light</u> it won't grow properly.
   - an organism may experience <u>trauma</u> (an <u>emotional shock</u> or a <u>physical injury</u>) which can
     affect their health, e.g. the sudden death of a loved one may cause <u>anxiety</u> and <u>depression</u>.
   - the organism's <u>lifestyle</u> may affect their health, e.g. eating too much food can lead to <u>obesity</u>.

Diseases Can be Communicable or Non-Communicable

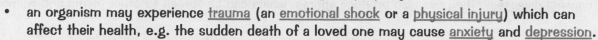
Communicable diseases are also known as infectious diseases.

1) A <u>communicable</u> disease is a disease that can <u>spread</u> between organisms.
   They are caused by <u>pathogens</u> infecting the organism. A <u>pathogen</u> is a type of <u>microorganism</u> that
   causes <u>disease</u>. Types of pathogen include <u>bacteria</u>, <u>viruses</u>, <u>protists</u> and <u>fungi</u> (see next page).

2) <u>Non-communicable</u> diseases <u>cannot</u> be passed from one organism to another, e.g. cardiovascular and
   respiratory diseases, cancers and diabetes. They generally last for a <u>long time</u> and <u>progress slowly</u>.
   They are associated with <u>genetic mutations</u>, <u>lifestyle</u> and <u>environmental factors</u> (see pages 24-25).

3) Both communicable and non-communicable diseases cause <u>symptoms</u> — <u>changes</u> in the organism
   that indicates disease is present. E.g. a symptom of <u>multiple sclerosis</u> (a disease that damages
   <u>nerve cells</u>) can be a temporary <u>loss of vision</u>.

4) However, symptoms may not <u>always</u> be obvious, especially in the early stages of a disease.
   For example, chicken pox is caused by a <u>virus</u>. Its main symptom is a <u>spotty rash</u>. Once a person
   has been <u>infected</u> with the virus, it takes around <u>14 days</u> for any spots to <u>appear</u> — this <u>time</u> between
   being <u>infected</u> with a pathogen and <u>showing</u> symptoms of the disease is called the <u>incubation period</u>.

Diseases May Interact With Each Other

Sometimes having <u>one disease</u> can make it <u>more or less likely</u> that you will suffer from <u>another disease</u>. E.g.

1) <u>HPV</u> (human papillomavirus) is a <u>virus</u> that can infect the <u>reproductive system</u>.
2) An <u>infection</u> by the virus <u>doesn't always</u> cause <u>symptoms</u> and often clears up on its own
   within a couple of months.
3) However, some <u>HPV infections</u> can cause <u>cell changes</u> resulting in the development of certain
   types of <u>cancer</u>. It's thought that <u>nearly all</u> cervical cancer cases result from HPV infections.

1) <u>Helminths</u> are a type of worm. If certain helminths get inside the human body, they can cause <u>disease</u>.
2) <u>Trichinosis</u> is a disease caused by infection by the helminth, *Trichinella spiralis*.
3) However, it's thought that infection by *Trichinella spiralis* may <u>reduce the development</u>
   of some <u>autoimmune diseases</u>, e.g. <u>Crohn's disease</u>.

Autoimmune diseases are diseases in which the body's immune system recognises the body's own cells as foreign, and attacks them.

I have a communicable disease — it's telling me to go to bed...

Communicable diseases can be <u>passed</u> between people because they involve <u>pathogens</u>.

Q1   What is meant by the term 'non-communicable' disease?   [1 mark]

How Disease Spreads

Well, here are loads of ways you can catch diseases. As if I wasn't feeling paranoid enough already...

Communicable Diseases are Caused by Pathogens

As you saw on the previous page, pathogens are microorganisms that cause communicable diseases. There are four types:

1) <u>BACTERIA</u> — <u>very small cells</u> (about 1/100th the size of your body cells), which can <u>reproduce rapidly</u>. They make you <u>feel ill</u> by <u>producing toxins</u> (poisons) that <u>damage your cells and tissues</u>.

2) <u>VIRUSES</u> — these are <u>not cells</u>. They're <u>really tiny</u>, about 1/100th the size of a bacterium. They replicate themselves <u>inside</u> the infected organism's cells. These cells then <u>burst</u>, <u>releasing</u> the <u>viruses</u>.

3) <u>PROTISTS</u> — these are <u>eukaryotic</u> (see page 2), usually <u>single-celled</u> and vary in size.

4) <u>FUNGI</u> — some fungi are <u>single-celled</u> while others have a <u>body</u>, which is made up of <u>thread-like structures</u> called <u>hyphae</u>. These hyphae can <u>grow</u> and <u>penetrate human skin</u> and the <u>surface of plants</u>, causing <u>diseases</u>. They can also produce <u>spores</u>, which can be spread to other plants and animals.

Communicable Diseases are Transmitted in Different Ways

Pathogens infect both <u>animals</u> and <u>plants</u> and can <u>spread</u> in different ways. For example:

Water	• Some pathogens can be picked up by drinking or bathing in <u>dirty water</u>. E.g. <u>Cholera</u> is a <u>bacterial infection</u> that causes <u>diarrhoea</u> and <u>dehydration</u>. It's spread when <u>drinking water</u> is <u>contaminated</u> with the diarrhoea of other sufferers.
Air	• Some pathogens are carried in the <u>air</u>. E.g. *Hymenoscyphus fraxineus* is a <u>fungus</u> which infects ash trees and causes <u>Chalara ash dieback</u> disease. It is transmitted from infected plants, through the <u>air</u>, by the <u>wind</u>. • Airborne pathogens can be carried in <u>droplets</u> produced when you <u>cough</u> or <u>sneeze</u> — so other people can <u>breathe them in</u>. E.g. the <u>influenza virus</u> that causes <u>flu</u> is spread this way.
On Surfaces	• Some pathogens can be picked up by <u>touching</u> contaminated surfaces. E.g. <u>tobacco mosaic disease</u> affects many species of plants, e.g. tomatoes. It's caused by a <u>virus</u> called <u>tobacco mosaic virus (TMV)</u> that makes the leaves of plants <u>mottled</u> and <u>discoloured</u>. The discolouration means the plant can't <u>photosynthesise</u> as well, so the virus affects <u>growth</u>. It's spread when <u>infected</u> leaves <u>rub</u> against <u>healthy</u> leaves. • <u>Athlete's foot</u> is a <u>fungal</u> disease which affects humans — it makes skin on the feet itch and flake off. It's most commonly spread by touching the same things as an infected person, e.g. <u>shower floors</u> and <u>towels</u>.
Body fluids	• Some pathogens are spread by <u>body fluids</u> such as <u>blood</u> (e.g. by <u>sharing needles</u> to inject drugs or by <u>contaminated blood transfusions</u>), <u>breast milk</u> (through breast feeding) and <u>semen</u> (through <u>unprotected sex</u> — diseases that are spread through sexual contact are known as <u>sexually transmitted infections</u> or <u>STIs</u>). <u>HIV</u> is a <u>virus</u> spread by <u>exchanging body fluids</u>. It initially causes <u>flu-like symptoms</u> for a few weeks, but after that, the person doesn't usually experience any symptoms for several years. The virus enters the <u>lymph nodes</u> and attacks the <u>immune cells</u>. If the immune system isn't working properly, it <u>can't cope</u> with <u>other infections</u> or <u>cancers</u>. At this stage, the virus is known as <u>late stage HIV</u>, or <u>AIDS</u>.
Animal vectors	• Animals that <u>spread disease</u> are called <u>vectors</u>. E.g. <u>malaria</u> is caused by a <u>protist</u>. Part of the malarial protist's <u>life cycle</u> takes place inside a mosquito. Mosquitoes act as <u>vectors</u> — they <u>pick up</u> the malarial protist when they <u>feed</u> on an <u>infected animal</u>. Every time the mosquito feeds on another animal, it <u>infects it</u> by inserting the protist into the animal's blood vessels. Malaria causes <u>repeating</u> episodes of <u>fever</u>. It can be <u>fatal</u>.
Soil	• Some <u>pathogens</u> can live in the <u>soil</u>, so plants in the <u>contaminated</u> soil may be <u>infected</u>. E.g. the bacteria, *Agrobacterium tumefaciens*, that cause <u>crown gall disease</u>, are able to <u>live freely</u> in some soils and on the <u>roots</u> of some plants. If the bacteria enter a plant, they can cause <u>growths</u> or <u>tumours</u> called <u>galls</u> on roots, stems and branches. The galls can <u>damage</u> the plant <u>tissue</u>, <u>restricting</u> the flow of <u>water</u> through the plant. This causes the plant to become <u>weaker</u> and it may eventually <u>die</u>.
Food	• Some pathogens are picked up by <u>eating contaminated food</u>. E.g. *Salmonella* bacteria are found in some foods, e.g. raw meat. If these foods are <u>kept too long</u> or <u>not cooked properly</u> the bacteria can cause <u>food poisoning</u>.

Ahh...Ahh... Ahhhhh Chooooooooo — urghh, this page is catching...

Pathogens are usually really small — you often need a microscope to see them — but they don't half get about...

Q1 Give three ways in which communicable diseases can be spread. [3 marks]

Defending Against Pathogens

Pathogens can be <u>anywhere</u>, so organisms have to be <u>on guard</u> at all times to make sure they don't get in.

Humans Have a Pretty Sophisticated Defence System

The human body has got features that <u>stop</u> a lot of nasties entering the <u>blood</u>. These are <u>non-specific</u> defences (they aren't produced in response to a <u>particular</u> pathogen) and they're <u>always present</u>. These can be <u>physical</u> (if they act as a physical <u>barrier</u> to pathogens), <u>chemical</u> (if they involve chemicals which <u>kill</u> pathogens) or <u>microbial</u> (if they involve <u>other</u> microorganisms). Here are some examples:

Physical

1) The whole <u>respiratory tract</u> (nasal passage, trachea and lungs) is lined with <u>mucus</u> and <u>cilia</u> (hair-like structures) — the mucus <u>traps</u> particles that could contain pathogens and the cilia <u>waft the mucus</u> up to the back of the throat where it can be <u>swallowed</u>.

2) The <u>skin</u> acts as a <u>barrier</u> to pathogens. If it gets cut, pathogens could enter the bloodstream through the wound. This is where platelets come in...

3) <u>Platelets</u> in the blood clump together to 'plug' the wound. This is known as <u>blood clotting</u>. Blood clots <u>stop you losing</u> too much <u>blood</u> and help to prevent <u>microorganisms</u> from entering the blood.

Platelets are <u>tiny fragments of cells</u>. They contain lots of <u>different substances</u> that are needed to help form the <u>clot</u>. They also have <u>proteins</u> on their surface which help them stick together and to the site of the wound.

Chemical

1) <u>Eyes</u> produce (in <u>tears</u>) an enzyme called <u>lysozyme</u>, which breaks down <u>bacteria</u> on the surface of the eye.

2) <u>Saliva</u> (produced in the <u>mouth</u>) contains molecules which <u>kill</u> pathogens that enter the mouth, so they don't reach the <u>stomach</u>.

3) The <u>stomach</u> produces <u>hydrochloric acid</u>. This <u>kills pathogens</u>.

Microbial

<u>Some</u> pathogens manage to make it past the <u>saliva</u> in the mouth and the <u>acid</u> in the stomach and enter the <u>gut</u>. Here, they have to compete with the <u>bacteria</u> which <u>naturally live in the gut</u> (<u>intestines</u>), in order to <u>survive</u>.

And even if pathogens <u>do</u> manage to make it past all of these defences to <u>enter the blood</u>, there's still a complex <u>immune system</u>, involving <u>antibodies</u> and <u>immune cells</u> (see next page) that they have to deal with.

Plants Also Have Physical Defences Against Pathogens...

1) Most plant <u>leaves</u> have a <u>waxy cuticle</u> (a thin transparent layer on the leaf's <u>upper surface</u>), which acts as a <u>waterproof barrier</u>. This barrier also <u>stops pathogens</u> entering the plant. The <u>cuticle</u> helps prevent <u>water collecting</u> on the leaf too, reducing the risk of infection by pathogens that are <u>transferred in water</u>.

2) Plant cells themselves are surrounded by <u>cell walls</u> made from <u>cellulose</u>. These form a <u>physical barrier</u> against pathogens that make it past the waxy cuticle.

...as Well as a Simple Immune System

Antimicrobial substances are chemicals that act against microorganisms — e.g. antibiotics (see p.28).

1) Plants <u>don't have</u> specialised immune cells or antibodies like <u>animals</u> (see next page). However, if a pathogen manages to cross their <u>physical defences</u>, they can <u>detect</u> it and <u>respond</u> by producing <u>antimicrobial substances</u> as a form of <u>chemical defence</u>. E.g. <u>phytoalexins</u> may be produced in <u>response</u> to infection by a pathogen — these are thought to <u>disrupt</u> the <u>metabolism</u> and <u>cell structure</u> of some species of <u>fungi</u> and <u>bacteria</u>.

2) Plants are at the <u>start</u> of nearly all <u>food chains</u> on Earth (see p.48), so the ability of plants to <u>defend</u> themselves against pathogens isn't just important for plants <u>themselves</u>, but also for <u>other</u> organisms.

3) For example, damage to <u>crops</u> by pathogens can threaten <u>human food security</u> (the availability of <u>nutritious</u> food for people — see p.96)

Drowning pathogens in soda — my preferred fizzy kill defence...

Admit it — plants are cleverer than you thought. There's lots to learn here so keep going over it 'til it sticks.

Q1 Give two physical methods that plants use to defend themselves against pathogens. [2 marks]

The Human Immune System

This page is all about white blood cells, or the ninjas of your body, as I like to call them. These little fellows can sneak up on pathogens in your blood, and kill them before they have a chance to cause you serious problems.

Your Immune System Can Attack Pathogens

1) If pathogens do make it into your body, your immune system kicks in to destroy them.

2) The most important part of your immune system is the white blood cells. They travel around in your blood and crawl into every part of you, constantly patrolling for pathogens.

3) Every cell has molecules on its surface called antigens. Each antigen is unique to the specific cell type that it's found on. White blood cells have special receptors in their membrane which help them to identify antigens on pathogens.

4) In a healthy person, white blood cells recognise antigens on pathogens as non-self (foreign) and antigens on normal body cells as self.

5) When they come across non-self antigens the immune system is triggered to destroy any invading pathogens. There are three main lines of attack:

1. Consuming Them

Some white blood cells (phagocytes) have a flexible membrane and contain lots of enzymes. This enables them to engulf (ingest) foreign cells and digest them. This is called phagocytosis.

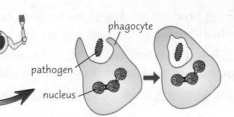

2. Producing Antibodies

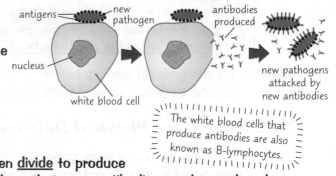

1) When white blood cells come across a foreign antigen on a pathogen, receptors in the membrane bind to the antigen. The white blood cells then start to produce proteins called antibodies which lock onto the antigens on the invading cells. The antibodies produced are specific to that type of antigen — they won't lock on to any others.

The white blood cells that produce antibodies are also known as B-lymphocytes.

2) The white blood cells that detect the pathogen then divide to produce more copies (clones) of the same white blood cell, so that more antibodies can be produced.

3) Antibodies are produced rapidly and are carried around the body to lock on to all similar pathogens.

4) The antibodies may disable the pathogen or 'tag' the pathogens, which helps the phagocytes find them so they can engulf them.

5) Some white blood cells stay around in the blood after the pathogen has been fought off — these are called memory cells. If the person is infected with the same pathogen again, the memory cells will trigger the rapid production of the antibodies needed to destroy it, before the pathogen causes the disease — the person is naturally immune to that pathogen and won't get ill.

3. Producing Antitoxins

Some pathogens can cause problems for the body by the toxins which they produce. Some white blood cells also produce antitoxins which counteract these toxins and so limit any damage done by the invading pathogens.

Fight disease — give your nose a blow with boxing gloves...

The body makes antibodies against the antigens on pathogens. There, don't say I never help you. Right, tea...

Q1 Give one role of antibodies in the immune response.   [1 mark]

Q2 Describe the role of memory cells in the immune response.   [2 marks]

Reducing and Preventing the Spread of Disease

The best way of dealing with disease is sometimes to just avoid any contact with pathogens in the first place...

The Spread of Disease Can Be Reduced or Prevented in Animals...

If a disease spreads uncontrollably, it can result in huge loss of life and food sources (if animals reared for food are affected). It's important that we take measures to prevent this from happening — including:

1) Being hygienic — basic hygiene measures (e.g. washing hands regularly to remove pathogens) can be very effective at preventing the spread of disease.

2) Sterilising wounds in the skin — this kills microorganisms (including pathogens) near the wound so stops them entering the blood.

> Many diseases are spread when a person touches a source of pathogens (e.g. door handle) and then touches their eyes, nose or mouth.

3) Living in sanitary conditions — having access to clean drinking water and a good system for disposing of sewage are both very effective measures for reducing the transmission of water-borne pathogens, such as cholera (see page 14), and pathogens in the urine or faeces of infected people. However, the initial cost to a society of creating sanitary conditions can be high.

4) Destroying infected animals — infected animals may pass on the disease to other individuals, so in some cases, such as on farms with large herds of animals, it might be necessary to kill the infected individuals to prevent large numbers of other animals from getting the disease. However, this is very costly and the disease may still spread if it is present in other individuals without symptoms.

5) Isolating infected individuals — this prevents them from passing it on to anyone else. In some cases, individuals should also be prevented from travelling, and spreading it even further. Although this benefits society, it can be difficult for an infected person as they can't be with their loved ones — sometimes it can be difficult to balance the needs of an individual while doing what is best for society.

6) Vaccination (see next page) — vaccinating people and animals against communicable diseases means that they won't develop the infection and then pass it on to others.

7) The use of contraception — using condoms prevents sexually transmitted infections, (e.g. HIV — see p.14) from being transmitted between people during sex.

... And in Plants

Plant diseases can reduce food sources for many organisms and can damage habitats for other organisms in an ecosystem. Here are some ways that the spread of disease in plants can be controlled:

1) Regulating movement of plant material — this makes sure that infected plants don't come into contact with healthy plants, e.g. plant nurseries are not allowed to sell plants which have crown gall disease.

2) Destroying infected plants — this stops them being sources of infection, but can be costly to a farmer.

3) Only using sources of healthy seeds and plants — this stops the disease from being introduced into a population.

4) Crop rotation — many pathogens are specific to a particular plant. Changing the type of plants that are grown stops the pathogens becoming established in an area. However, it may limit how profitable a farm is if it has to change farming practices for a different crop each year.

5) Polyculture (growing different types plants in a single area at the same time) — if a pathogen specific to a single plant enters one plant, it's less likely to infect neighbouring plants because they are different species — limiting the spread of the pathogen through the crop.

6) Chemical control — for example, fungicides can be used to kill fungal pathogens. This can be an effective method but may also lead to the evolution of resistant strains of the pathogen (see page 87).

7) Biological control — this is when another organism is used to control a pest or pathogen. For example, ladybirds eat aphids (an insect pest) so ladybirds can be released into an area to reduce aphid numbers. However, in some cases, the control organism may become a pest itself and cause more problems.

The spread of disease — mouldy margarine...

Make sure you understand how each method above can be effective in preventing the spread of disease. However, you should also be aware of any costs associated with them, whether to an individual or to society as a whole.

Q1   Give one benefit and one cost to a farmer of using a crop rotation system.   [2 marks]

Vaccinations

Before you get cracking on this page, take a look back at p.16 to remind yourself about the <u>immune response</u>.

Vaccinations Stop You Getting Infections

1) When you're infected with a <u>new</u> pathogen it can take your white blood cells a while to produce the <u>antibodies</u> to deal with it. In that time you can get <u>very ill</u>, or maybe even die.

2) To avoid this you can be <u>vaccinated</u> (immunised) against some diseases, e.g. polio or measles.

3) Vaccination Involves injecting <u>dead, inactive or weakened</u> pathogens into the body. These carry <u>antigens</u>, so even though they're <u>harmless</u> they still trigger an <u>immune response</u> — your white blood cells produce <u>antibodies</u> to attack them.

4) Some of these white blood cells will remain in the blood as <u>memory cells</u>, so if <u>live</u> pathogens of the <u>same type</u> ever appear, the antibodies that <u>help destroy them</u> will be produced immediately.

5) Big outbreaks of disease — called <u>epidemics</u> — can be prevented if a <u>large percentage</u> of the population is vaccinated. That way, even the people who aren't vaccinated are <u>unlikely</u> to catch the disease because there are <u>fewer</u> people able to <u>pass it on</u>. But if a significant number of people <u>aren't</u> vaccinated, the disease can <u>spread</u> quickly through them and lots of people will be <u>ill</u> at the same time.

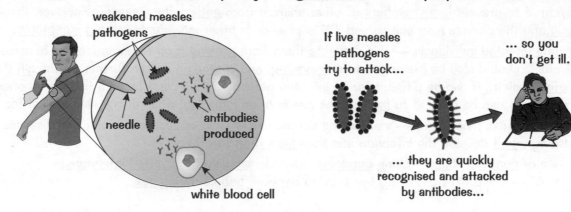

weakened measles pathogens

needle

antibodies produced

white blood cell

If live measles pathogens try to attack...

... they are quickly recognised and attacked by antibodies...

... so you don't get ill.

There are Pros and Cons of Vaccination

PROS

Vaccines have helped <u>control</u> lots of communicable diseases that were once <u>common</u> in the UK (e.g. polio, measles, whooping cough, rubella, mumps, tetanus...). <u>Smallpox</u> no longer occurs at all, and <u>polio</u> infections have fallen by 99%.

CONS

1) Vaccines don't always work — sometimes they <u>don't</u> give you <u>immunity</u>.

2) You can sometimes have a <u>bad reaction</u> to a vaccine (e.g. swelling, or maybe something more serious like a fever or seizures). But bad reactions are very <u>rare</u>.

3) It can be <u>expensive</u> to make vaccines and carry out <u>vaccination programmes</u> — if a disease occurs only very <u>rarely</u> or the vaccine isn't very <u>effective</u>, the cost of carrying out the programme may <u>outweigh</u> any benefits to society.

Some people are concerned that using whole pathogens in vaccines (even though they are dead, weakened or inactive) could still cause disease. Some vaccines therefore only use parts of cells, to avoid these concerns.

Take that, you evil antigen...

Deciding whether to have a vaccination means balancing risks — the risk of catching the disease if you don't have a vaccine, against the risk of having a bad reaction if you do. As always, you need to look at the evidence. For example, if you get measles (the disease), there's about a 1 in 15 chance that you'll get complications (e.g. pneumonia) — and about 1 in 500 people who get measles actually die. However, the number of people who have a problem with the vaccine is more like 1 in 1 000 000.

Q1   Explain how white blood cells respond to vaccinations.   [2 marks]

Detecting Diseases

Sometimes it can be pretty obvious that an organism has a disease, but it can be important to work out exactly what disease it has in order to treat it properly.

Diseases Can be Detected and Identified in the Field

1) In some cases, simply observing an organism's symptoms can indicate what disease it has.

2) For example, a plant pathologist (an expert in plant disease) may recognise the symptoms of different plant diseases — e.g. growths on roots, stems or branches might indicate crown gall disease.

3) Experts in human or animal health might also recognise the symptoms of certain diseases, e.g. a high temperature and spotty rash may indicate chicken pox.

4) However, sometimes the observable symptoms may not be enough to allow the disease to be properly identified — especially if the symptoms could indicate many different diseases or the symptoms are uncommon. That's where laboratory techniques comes in...

Fever (a very high body temperature) is a symptom of many different diseases. It can help the body fight infection by killing pathogens or reducing the speed at which they can multiply.

Laboratory Techniques Can be Used to Identify a Disease

1) Laboratory techniques can help to identify which disease an organism has and identify the pathogen that's causing it. This is important so that the most appropriate treatment can be given.

2) Samples of tissue or body fluids (e.g. blood, urine or faeces) from the diseased organism can be taken and analysed in the following ways:

1) Counting the number of cells in a sample — e.g. some diseases may change the number of red blood cells (see page 71) in a given volume of blood, so a red blood cell count may help to identify the presence of a particular disease. The number of white blood cells is also important — a number outside the normal range can indicate that the body is fighting an infection.

2) Viewing a sample using a microscope (see page 3) — scientists may be able to identify particular microorganisms present in the sample from their appearance. Staining the sample may also help to highlight and identify any pathogens — e.g. some species of bacteria will absorb a dye and become stained, while others won't — this property can help to identify which species of bacteria is present.

3) Growing the sample in a culture (see next page) — sometimes there may not be enough of the pathogen in a sample to be identified under a microscope. By adding the sample to a growth medium and allowing any microorganisms within it to multiply, they will be more likely to be observed.

4) Testing microorganisms found in the sample with antimicrobial compounds — the effectiveness of different antimicrobials (e.g. antibiotics) in killing the microorganism may help to identify it.

5) Sequencing and analysing the genetic material (see page 9) of microorganisms in the sample — scientists have worked out the genomes of many different pathogens. Laboratory tests can find out if a specific pathogen is present in a sample by adding sections of DNA which are known to be complementary to the pathogen's DNA to the sample. If the pathogen is present, the DNA strands will bind to the pathogen's DNA and allow it to be identified.

6) Isolation and reinfection (in plants) — a section of diseased plant tissue can be added to a growth medium in the lab — this will encourage microorganisms to grow. Scientists can then isolate the microorganism they suspect is causing the disease and infect healthy plants with it — if the healthy plants develop the same symptoms as the diseased plant, the pathogen causing the disease has been identified.

You can also use monoclonal antibodies to detect a pathogen — see p.22.

3) Throughout all laboratory tests, it's important that aseptic techniques are used — see next page. These ensure that the samples from the diseased organism don't get contaminated with other microorganisms — this could lead to the wrong microorganism being detected as the pathogen causing the disease.

Symptoms of revision deficiency include nagging parents...

It's important to identify exactly what's causing an organism to be unwell so that the right treatments can be given.

Q1   Describe how staining can help to identify a bacterial species in a sample under a microscope.   [2 marks]

PRACTICAL Culturing Microorganisms

Here's how you can grow microorganisms and test how effective different antibiotics are at killing them.

You Can Grow Bacteria in the Lab

1) Bacteria (and some other microorganisms) are grown (cultured) in a "culture medium", which contains the carbohydrates, minerals, proteins and vitamins they need to grow.

2) The culture medium used can be a nutrient broth solution or solid agar jelly.

3) Bacteria grown on agar 'plates' will form visible colonies on the surface of the jelly, or will spread out to give an even covering of bacteria.

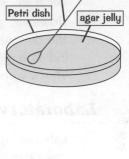

- To make an agar plate, hot agar jelly is poured into a shallow round plastic dish called a Petri dish.
- When the jelly's cooled and set, an inoculating loop (wire loop) can be used to transfer microorganisms to the culture medium. Alternatively, a sterile dropping pipette and spreader can be used to get an even covering of bacteria.
- The microorganisms then multiply.

4) In the lab at school, cultures of microorganisms are not kept above 25 °C, because harmful pathogens are more likely to grow above this temperature.

5) In industrial conditions, cultures are incubated at higher temperatures so that they can grow a lot faster.

You Can Investigate the Effect of Antibiotics on Bacterial Growth

Antibiotics are substances which kill or reduce the growth of bacteria. You can test the action of antibiotics on cultures of bacteria:

1) Place paper discs soaked in different types (or different concentrations) of antibiotics on an agar plate that has an even covering of bacteria. Leave some space between the discs.

2) The antibiotic should diffuse (soak) into the agar jelly. Antibiotic-resistant bacteria (i.e. bacteria that aren't affected by the antibiotic — see p.87) will continue to grow on the agar around the paper discs, but non-resistant strains will die. A clear zone will be left where the bacteria have died.

3) Make sure you use a control. This is a paper disc that has not been soaked in an antibiotic. Instead, soak it in sterile water. You can then be sure that any difference between the growth of the bacteria around the control disc and around one of the antibiotic discs is due to the effect of the antibiotic alone (and not, e.g. something in the paper).

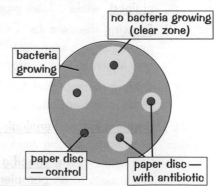

4) Leave the plate for 48 hours at 25 °C.

5) The more effective the antibiotic is against the bacteria, the larger the clear zone will be — see next page.

You Need to Use Aseptic Techniques

Aseptic techniques are used to prevent contamination of cultures by unwanted microorganisms. This would affect your results and could potentially result in the growth of pathogens. To avoid this:

1) The Petri dishes and culture medium must be sterilised before use (e.g. by heating to a high temperature) to kill any unwanted microorganisms that may be lurking on them.

2) If an inoculating loop is used to transfer the bacteria to the culture medium, it should be sterilised first by carefully passing it through a hot flame.

3) Work near a Bunsen flame. Hot air rises, so any microorganisms in the air should be drawn away from your culture.

4) After transferring the bacteria, the lid of the Petri dish should be lightly taped on — to stop microorganisms from the air getting in.

5) The Petri dish should be stored upside down — to stop drops of condensation falling onto the agar surface.

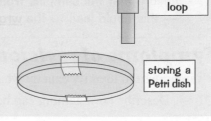

Chapter B2 — Keeping Healthy

Culturing Microorganisms PRACTICAL

Calculate the Sizes of the Clear Zones to Compare Results

1) You can <u>compare</u> the <u>effectiveness</u> of different antibiotics on bacteria by looking at the <u>relative sizes</u> of the <u>clear zones</u>.

2) The <u>larger</u> the clear zone around a disc, the <u>more effective</u> the antibiotic is against the bacteria.

3) You can do this <u>by eye</u> if there are large differences in size. But to get more accurate results it's a good idea to calculate the <u>area</u> of the clear zones using their <u>diameter</u> (the distance <u>across</u>).

4) To calculate the area of a clear zone, you need to use <u>this equation</u>:

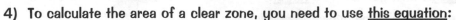

This is the equation for the area of a circle. You're likely to use the units cm² or mm².

$$Area = \pi r^2$$

r is the radius of the clear zone — it's equal to half the diameter.

π is just a number. You should have a button for it on your calculator. If not, just use the value 3.14.

Don't open the Petri dish to measure the clear zones — they should be visible through the bottom of the dish.

EXAMPLE: The diagram below shows the clear zones produced by antibiotics A and B. Use the areas of the clear zones to compare the effectiveness of the antibiotics.

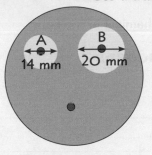

A 14 mm B 20 mm

Diagram not to scale.

1) Divide the diameter of zone A by <u>two</u> to find the <u>radius</u>.

2) Stick the radius value into the <u>equation</u> area = πr^2.

3) <u>Repeat</u> steps 1 and 2 for zone B.

4) <u>Compare</u> the <u>sizes</u> of the <u>areas</u>. 314 mm² is just over twice 154 mm², so you could say that:

Radius of A = 14 ÷ 2 = 7 mm

Area of A = π × 7² = 154 mm²

Radius of B = 20 ÷ 2 = 10 mm

Area of B = π × 10² = 314 mm²

The clear zone of antibiotic B is roughly twice the size of the clear zone of antibiotic A.

You Can Also Find the Area of a Colony

The equation above can also be used to calculate the <u>area</u> of a bacterial <u>colony</u>. You just need to measure the <u>diameter</u> of the colony you are interested in first.

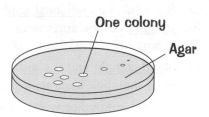

One colony

Agar

Agar — my favourite jelly flavour after raspberry...

Microorganisms might be the perfect pets. You don't have to walk them, they won't get lonely and they hardly cost anything to feed. But whatever you do, do not feed them after midnight.

Q1 A researcher was investigating the effect of three different antibiotics on the growth of bacteria. The diagram on the right shows the results.

a) Which antibiotic was most effective against the bacteria? [1 mark]

b) Calculate the size of the clear zone for Antibiotic C. Give your answer in mm². [2 marks]

c) Describe a control that could have been used for this investigation. [1 mark]

d) Explain why a control should be used. [1 mark]

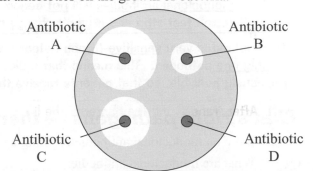

Antibiotic A

Antibiotic B

Antibiotic C

Antibiotic D

Monoclonal Antibodies

Right, onto something new now — monoclonal antibodies. _Antibodies_ (see page 16) aren't only used by our _immune systems_ — scientists have engineered them for lots of _new uses_. Intrigued — read on...

Monoclonal Antibodies are Identical Antibodies

1) Antibodies are produced by white blood cells (see page 16).

2) Monoclonal antibodies are produced from lots of clones of a single white blood cell. This means all the antibodies are identical and will only target one specific protein antigen.

3) To make monoclonal antibodies, an animal (usually a mouse) is first injected with the antigen which you want to target.

4) The white blood cells in the mouse which recognise the antigen will then start to divide and produce antibodies against it.

5) A sample of blood is taken from the mouse and the cells producing the right antibody extracted from the sample.

6) The cells are fused with tumour cells (which can divide many times, see p.24). The resulting cells are placed in a culture medium and divide. This produces many cells that can produce lots of the antibody.

7) You can make monoclonal antibodies that bind to anything, e.g. an antigen that's only found on one type of cell. They will only bind to this molecule — so you can use them to target a specific cell or chemical in the body.

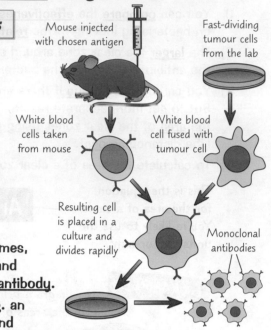

Mouse injected with chosen antigen

Fast-dividing tumour cells from the lab

White blood cells taken from mouse

White blood cell fused with tumour cell

Resulting cell is placed in a culture and divides rapidly

Monoclonal antibodies

Monoclonal Antibodies Can Be Used to Identify Pathogens

You can make monoclonal antibodies that will detect the presence of a particular pathogen to help in diagnosing a disease. For example:

1) Malaria is a disease caused by a pathogen called _Plasmodium falciparum_, which is found in the blood of infected people. The pathogen can be detected in a sample of blood using a diagnostic stick.

2) A sample of blood is added to one end of the stick, which contains monoclonal antibodies specific to the antigens on the surface of _Plasmodium_. These antibodies are also labelled with a dye.

3) The blood sample and the antibodies move along the length of the stick towards a test strip.

4) Monoclonal antibodies which also recognise the _Plasmodium_ antigens are stuck to the test strip.

5) If the pathogen is present in the blood sample, then the antibodies on the test strip and the antibodies which are stuck to the dye will bind to the pathogen's antigens and the test strip will change colour.

6) If the pathogen is not present then the labelled monoclonal antibodies will not become stuck to the test strip and it won't change colour.

blood sample added here

test strip

antibody bound to a coloured dye

antibody stuck down

Pathogen IS present:

antibody binds to antigen

liquid flows along stick...

...and dye becomes stuck to test strip.

Pathogen is NOT present:

liquid flows along stick...

...but dye doesn't stick.

This method is very sensitive (it can detect even small amounts of a pathogen in a sample) and it's specific to only one pathogen. This means that a diagnosis can be made much faster and more accurately than was previously possible, so that patients receive the correct treatment sooner.

That's right pathogens — there's nowhere to hide now...

There's more on monoclonal antibodies coming up next, but don't move on until you understand this page.

Q1   What are monoclonal antibodies?   [1 mark]

More on Monoclonal Antibodies

Because monoclonal antibodies can be produced to <u>target</u> a <u>specific</u> chemical or cell, they have loads of uses. You need to know how they can be used to <u>treat cancer</u>.

You Can Use Monoclonal Antibodies to Treat Cancer

1) As well as using monoclonal antibodies to help <u>diagnose</u> a disease (see previous page), can also use them to help <u>treat</u> a disease, such as cancer.

2) Monoclonal antibodies can be designed to <u>specifically target</u> a certain <u>cell-type</u> in the body (e.g. just cancer cells). So you can use them to <u>label specific cells</u> for <u>destruction</u> by the immune system, or use them to <u>target drugs</u> to specific locations in the body.

3) Cancer cells have <u>antigens</u> on their <u>cell membranes</u> that <u>aren't</u> found on normal body cells. They're called <u>tumour markers</u>.

4) However, as cancer cells are <u>produced</u> by the <u>body</u> the tumour markers aren't <u>recognised</u> as '<u>foreign</u>' by the body's immune system. This means that they're <u>not attacked</u> by the <u>white blood cells</u> in the immune response (see page 16).

5) In the lab, <u>monoclonal antibodies</u> that will <u>bind</u> to tumour markers can be <u>made</u> and used to treat certain cancers.

Monoclonal Antibodies Can Trigger a Normal Immune Response...

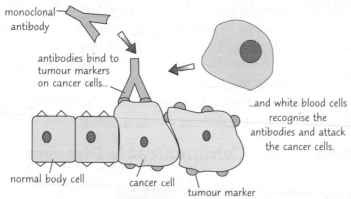

monoclonal antibody

antibodies bind to tumour markers on cancer cells...

...and white blood cells recognise the antibodies and attack the cancer cells.

normal body cell   cancer cell   tumour marker

1) Monoclonal antibodies can be <u>injected</u> into a patient's <u>bloodstream</u>.

2) The antibodies will then bind to the <u>tumour markers</u> on cancer cells in the patient's body.

3) For <u>some</u> types of monoclonal antibody, this will result in the cancer cells being <u>labelled</u>, causing a normal <u>immune response</u> to the cells — the patient's <u>white blood cells</u> will <u>recognise</u> the cancer cells as foreign and <u>destroy them</u>.

...or Target Drugs to Cancer Cells

1) An <u>anti-cancer drug</u> is attached to monoclonal antibodies. This might be a <u>radioactive</u> or a <u>toxic substance</u> which stops cancer cells <u>growing</u> and <u>dividing</u>.

2) The antibodies are <u>injected</u> into the patient's <u>bloodstream</u> and bind to the <u>tumour markers</u> on the <u>cancer cells</u>.

3) The drug <u>kills</u> the <u>cancer cells</u> but <u>doesn't</u> kill any <u>normal body cells</u> near the tumour.

4) Other cancer treatments, such as <u>radiotherapy</u> and <u>chemotherapy</u>, <u>can</u> affect normal host cells as well as killing cancer cells. This often leads to unpleasant <u>side effects</u>, such as <u>hair loss</u> and <u>vomiting</u>.

5) Since <u>antibody-based</u> drugs are <u>targeted directly</u> to the <u>cancer</u> cells, <u>side effects</u> tend to be less severe than for radiotherapy or chemotherapy treatments.

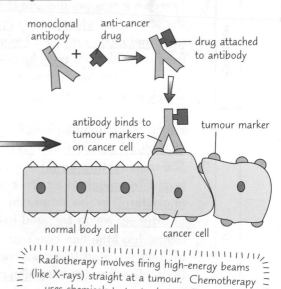

monoclonal antibody   anti-cancer drug

drug attached to antibody

antibody binds to tumour markers on cancer cell

tumour marker

normal body cell   cancer cell

Radiotherapy involves firing high-energy beams (like X-rays) straight at a tumour. Chemotherapy uses chemicals to try to destroy the tumour.

Bonoclonal antibodies — used to detect Irish rock stars...

By now I think you'll agree that monoclonal antibodies are pretty useful. Make sure you understand both of the ways they can be used to treat cancer — either by triggering a normal immune response or by delivering drugs.

Q1   Explain how monoclonal antibodies can be used to deliver drugs to cancer cells.   [3 marks]

Non-Communicable Diseases

You may remember non-communicable diseases from page 13. Well, here's a bit more about them...

Lots of Factors Interact to Cause Non-Communicable Diseases

1) All diseases have risk factors — things that increase a person's chance of getting that disease. Risk factors are often aspects of a person's lifestyle (e.g. how much exercise they do). They can also be the presence of certain substances in the environment (e.g. a person's work may mean they are more exposed to certain pollutants in the air, which could increase the risk of getting lung cancer) or a person's genes (specific genetic variants — see page 6 — may make it more or less likely for a person to get a particular disease).

2) Many non-communicable diseases (such as some cancers, cardiovascular disease (CVD) (diseases of the heart or blood vessels, see p.29), some lung diseases, liver diseases, and some nutrition-related diseases, e.g. type 2 diabetes, see p.82) are caused by several different risk factors interacting with each other rather than one factor alone. For example:

> Normally, when cells have divided enough times to make enough new cells, they stop. But if there's a mutation in a gene that controls cell division, the cells can grow out of control. The cells keep on dividing by mitosis to make more and more cells, which form a tumour. Cancer is a tumour that invades surrounding tissue.

> Sometimes you can inherit genetic variants that make you more susceptible to cancer. The genes alone don't mean you will get cancer but the chance is increased if you have other risk factors too, such as poor diet, high alcohol consumption and smoking (see below and next page).

Loads of things are known to be risk factors for cancer, e.g. HPV (see p.13), UV exposure, radiation, etc.

3) Risk factors are identified by scientists looking for correlations in data, but correlation doesn't always equal cause (see p.107). Sometimes a risk factor is linked to another factor, and it's this other factor that actually causes the disease. For example, a lack of exercise and a high fat diet are heavily linked to an increased chance of CVD, but they can't cause it directly. It's the resulting high blood pressure and high 'bad' cholesterol levels (see below) that can actually cause it.

4) There are some examples where scientists have found evidence to support a risk factor being a cause of a disease though, e.g. the fact that smoking can cause lung disease and lung cancer (see next page).

Lifestyle Factors Can Affect the Risk of Non-Communicable Diseases

Exercise

1) Exercise increases the amount of energy used by the body and decreases the amount of stored body fat. It also builds muscle, which helps to boost your metabolic rate — a higher metabolic rate means that energy from food is used more quickly. So people who exercise regularly are less likely to suffer from health problems such as obesity (see below) and CVD.

2) A lack of exercise increases the risk of CVD because it increases blood pressure.

There's more on the beneficial effects of regular exercise on page 27.

Diet

1) Eating too much can lead to obesity. Obesity is linked to type 2 diabetes, high blood pressure and CVD. It's also a risk factor for some cancers.

2) Too much saturated fat in your diet can increase your blood cholesterol level. Too much of a certain type of cholesterol (known as 'bad' or LDL cholesterol) in the blood can cause fatty deposits to form on the inside wall of arteries, which can lead to coronary heart disease (see p.29).

3) Eating too little can also cause problems. Malnutrition caused by a lack of food can lead to issues such as fatigue and poor resistance to infection. Some diseases (called deficiency diseases) can be caused by a lack of certain vitamins or minerals. E.g. scurvy is caused by a lack of vitamin C — it leads to problems with the skin, joints and gums.

4) However, eating a healthy, balanced diet that is rich in fruit and vegetables can reduce your risk of getting many non-communicable diseases, such as CVD and obesity.

Obesity is defined as being >20% over the maximum recommended body mass.

People whose diet is badly out of balance are said to be malnourished.

Best put down that cake and go for a run...

If you're amazed at all the different risk factors for non-communicable diseases then you'll just love the next page.

Q1 Give two lifestyle factors that can increase the risk of obesity. [2 marks]

More on Non-Communicable Diseases

Unfortunately, you're not finished with <u>risk factors</u> for <u>non-communicable diseases</u> yet. Here are some more...

Alcohol and Smoking Can Also Lead to Non-Communicable Diseases

Alcohol

1) <u>Alcohol</u> is <u>poisonous</u>. It's <u>broken down</u> by <u>enzymes</u> in the liver and some of the <u>products</u> are <u>toxic</u>. If you drink <u>too much</u> alcohol over a <u>long period</u> of time these toxic products can cause the <u>death</u> of liver cells, forming <u>scar tissue</u> that stops <u>blood</u> reaching the liver — this is called <u>cirrhosis</u>.

2) Drinking too much alcohol <u>increases blood pressure</u> which can lead to <u>CVD</u>.

3) Many <u>cancers</u> including those of the <u>mouth</u>, <u>throat</u>, <u>bowels</u> and <u>liver</u> have all been linked to alcohol consumption because the toxic products <u>damage DNA</u> and cause cells to <u>divide faster</u> than normal.

Smoking

Burning cigarettes produce <u>nicotine</u>, which is what makes smoking <u>addictive</u>. They also produce <u>carbon monoxide</u>, <u>tar</u>, and <u>particulates</u> — which can all cause <u>illness</u> and other <u>problems</u>. E.g.

1) <u>CVD</u> — <u>carbon monoxide</u> reduces the oxygen carrying capacity of the blood. If the <u>cardiac muscle</u> doesn't receive enough oxygen it can lead to a <u>heart attack</u> (see page 29). Nicotine increases <u>heart rate</u>. The heart contracts more often increasing <u>blood pressure</u>, which also increases the risk of <u>CVD</u>.

2) <u>Lung</u>, <u>throat</u>, <u>mouth</u> and <u>oesophageal cancer</u> — <u>tar</u> from cigarette smoke is full of toxic chemicals, some of which are <u>carcinogens</u> (cause <u>cancer</u>). Carcinogens make <u>mutations</u> in the DNA <u>more likely</u>, which can lead to <u>uncontrolled cell division</u> (see previous page).

3) Lung diseases, such as <u>chronic bronchitis</u> — cigarette smoke can cause <u>inflammation</u> of the lining of the <u>bronchi</u> and <u>bronchioles</u> (tubes in the lungs), which can result in <u>permanent damage</u>. Symptoms of chronic bronchitis include a <u>persistent cough</u> and <u>breathing problems</u>.

4) <u>Smoking</u> when <u>pregnant</u> can cause <u>lots</u> of <u>health problems</u> for the <u>unborn baby</u>.

Lifestyle Factors Cause Different Trends

Global

Non-communicable diseases are <u>more common</u> in <u>developed countries</u>, where people generally have a <u>higher income</u>, than in <u>developing countries</u>. However, these diseases are now becoming much <u>more common</u> in <u>developing</u> countries too. Different <u>lifestyle factors</u> contribute to these trends, but a lot of it is to do with <u>income</u>. For example:

- <u>Lack of exercise</u> and <u>higher alcohol consumption</u> are associated with <u>higher income</u>.
- <u>Smoking</u> varies massively between countries, but smoking-related deaths are <u>more common</u> in <u>poorer countries</u>.
- In both developed and developing countries, <u>obesity</u> is associated with <u>higher incomes</u> as people are able to afford lots of <u>high-fat food</u>. However, obesity is now associated with <u>lower incomes</u> too, as people are eating <u>cheaper</u>, <u>less healthy</u> foods.

National

Non-communicable diseases are the <u>biggest cause of death</u> in the <u>UK</u>. However, there are <u>differences</u> across the country. For example:

- People from <u>deprived areas</u> are much <u>more likely to smoke</u>, have a <u>poor diet</u>, and <u>not</u> take part in <u>physical activity</u> than those who are better off financially. This means that the incidence of heart disease, obesity, type 2 diabetes, and cancers is higher in those areas. People from deprived areas are also more likely to suffer from <u>alcohol-related disorders</u>.

Local

<u>Individual lifestyle choices</u> affect the incidence of non-communicable diseases at the local level — if you choose to smoke, drink, not take part in exercise or have a poor diet, then the <u>risk increases</u>.

Too many exams are a risk factor for stress...

Trends in non-communicable diseases are often to do with income, because it can have a big effect on lifestyle.

Q1   Suggest what kind of impact increasing cigarette prices may have on the prevalence of lung cancer at a national level. Explain your answer.   [2 marks]

Interpreting Data on Disease

In the exam, you could be given some data about the <u>causes</u>, <u>spread</u>, <u>effects</u> or <u>treatment</u> of disease. You'll need to be able to <u>interpret</u> the data (i.e. work out what it's showing) — this page should help you.

You Need to be Able to Interpret a Scatter Diagram

In a <u>scatter diagram</u>, <u>one variable</u> is plotted against a <u>second variable</u>, allowing you to easily spot if there's a <u>correlation</u> (a relationship) between the two variables. Both variables have to be <u>numbers</u>. For example:

There's more on correlations and scatter diagrams on page 104.

1) This scatter diagram shows the <u>prevalence of nonalcoholic fatty liver disease (NAFLD)</u> plotted against the <u>prevalence of obesity</u> for the general population of <u>nine different countries</u>.

2) The two variables are <u>positively correlated</u> with each other, as the values for both variables go in the <u>same direction</u> — i.e. as the prevalence of NAFLD goes up, so does the prevalence of obesity. The <u>line of best fit</u> helps to show this relationship (the <u>closer</u> the points are to the line, the <u>stronger</u> the correlation).

3) However, the golden rule to remember is that <u>correlation does not equal cause</u> (see p.107).

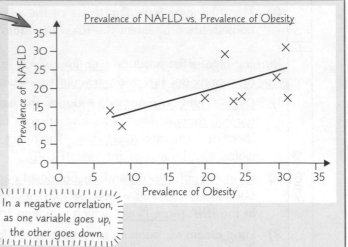

Prevalence of NAFLD vs. Prevalence of Obesity

In a negative correlation, as one variable goes up, the other goes down.

Data Can be Illustrated in Lots of Ways

1) There are lots of different ways that data can be <u>displayed</u>, e.g. data might be shown in a <u>numerical</u> form and displayed in a <u>table</u>, as shown here.

2) The <u>same</u> data can also be shown on a <u>graph</u>, e.g. a bar graph.

3) In the exam you might have to <u>translate</u> between different forms of data. For example, you might be given a <u>table</u> of data and be asked to <u>draw a graph</u> using the data. Or you might be <u>shown a graph</u> and be asked to give <u>numerical</u> data from it. You could also be given <u>frequency tables</u> or <u>histograms</u>.

4) Whatever you're asked to do, make sure you pay close attention to any <u>titles</u> in the table or <u>axes labels</u> on the graph, and to the <u>units</u> used.

Level of LDL cholesterol in blood (mg/dl)	>97.6-115.4	>115.4-132.2	>132.2-153.9	>153.9
Relative risk of cardiovascular event	0.9	1.1	1.3	1.5

A histogram looks a bit like a bar chart, but you need to calculate the area of each bar to interpret it, rather than just look at its height.

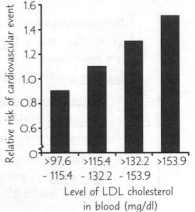

Health Data Has to be Collected Carefully

1) When studying issues about <u>health and disease</u>, e.g. risk factors for non-communicable diseases, it isn't possible to collect all of the <u>potential data</u> (data can't be collected from <u>every</u> member of the population). Instead data has to be collected from a <u>sample</u> that <u>represents</u> the full <u>potential</u> data set.

2) The <u>bigger</u> the sample <u>size</u> the <u>better</u>, as it's <u>more likely</u> that more of the different <u>characteristics</u> present in the <u>whole</u> population will be <u>included</u> in the sample. The sample should also be <u>random</u> to <u>avoid bias</u>. E.g. in a study looking at the effect of an <u>unhealthy diet</u> on the risk of <u>CVD</u>, it would be no good collecting the data by questioning people as they leave the <u>gym</u> (as gym-goers may not <u>represent</u> the whole population).

I thought illustrating data just meant colouring in the table...

Don't be frightened by any questions where you need to interpret data — just take your time and make sure you really understand what the data's showing you before you answer the questions.

Q1   Explain why a large sample size is better than a small one when collecting health data.   [1 mark]

Investigating Pulse Rate

So, a fun experiment to do now — grab your <u>headband</u> and <u>leg warmers</u> and let's get started...

You Can Investigate The Effect of Exercise on Pulse Rate | PRACTICAL

1) When you <u>exercise</u>, more energy is needed by your muscles to allow them to <u>contract more</u>.

Respiration is the process that transfers energy to your cells — it usually requires oxygen (see p.57).

2) This means your <u>rate of respiration has to increase</u>, so you need to get <u>more oxygen</u> into your cells.

3) Your <u>heart rate increases</u> to speed up the delivery of <u>oxygenated blood</u> to muscles.

4) You can do an <u>experiment</u> to investigate how exercise affects <u>heart rate</u>. E.g.

Your pulse rate is a way of measuring your heart rate. You can find it by putting two fingers on the inside of your wrist or your neck and counting the number of pulses in 1 minute.

> 1) Measure and record your <u>pulse rate</u> at <u>rest</u>.
>
> 2) Then do 3 minutes of <u>gentle exercise</u>, e.g. walk around your school field.
>
> 3) Measure and record your pulse rate again <u>immediately after</u> the exercise.
>
> 4) Then take <u>regular measurements</u> of your pulse rate until it has returned to its <u>resting rate</u>. Record the time that this takes — this is called the <u>recovery rate</u>.
>
> 5) Repeat steps 2-4 two times more, but <u>increase the intensity</u> of the exercise each time (e.g. jog round the field, then run round it).
>
> 6) Produce a <u>bar chart</u> of your results to show how <u>pulse rate</u> is affected by the <u>intensity of the exercise</u>. To <u>reduce</u> the effect of <u>random errors</u> on the results, collect anonymised results from the <u>whole class</u> and plot the <u>average percentage change in pulse rate</u> for each exercise. Do the same to show how <u>recovery rate</u> is affected by the intensity of exercise.
>
> 7) Remember to <u>control any variables</u> during the experiment, e.g. if you're using results from the whole class, make sure everyone's done the <u>same exercise activities</u> and for the <u>same length of time</u>.

Regular Exercise Can Reduce the Risk of Some Non-Communicable Diseases

1) A <u>high</u> resting heart rate and a <u>slow</u> recovery rate have both been linked to an <u>increased risk</u> of developing some <u>non-communicable diseases</u>, such as <u>CVD</u>.

2) <u>Regular exercise</u> can <u>reduce</u> a person's <u>resting heart rate</u> and <u>speed up</u> their <u>recovery rate</u>, and so could help to <u>reduce</u> the chance of them developing some non-communicable diseases.

3) Scientists are able to <u>investigate the link</u> between regular exercise and a lower resting heart rate and faster recovery rate using <u>long term studies</u>. For example, scientists could:

> 1) Recruit a <u>large number</u> of volunteers that <u>do not</u> exercise regularly.
>
> 2) Record the <u>resting heart rate</u> for <u>each</u> volunteer, then ask the volunteers to all do the <u>same</u> exercise activity and record the <u>recovery rate</u> of each of the volunteers.
>
> 3) Split the group in <u>half</u>, and ask one group to <u>continue</u> with their normal lifestyles and the other group to <u>exercise regularly</u> for 3 months — e.g. take a brisk 30 minute walk, 5 times a week.
>
> 4) At the <u>end</u> of the trial period, ask the volunteers to <u>come back</u> and then <u>repeat step 2</u>.
>
> 5) <u>Analyse</u> the data.

4) Studies such as this can help scientists to determine what <u>kind of exercise</u> or <u>length of training programme</u> is <u>most effective</u> for improving a person's <u>resting heart rate</u> and <u>recovery rate</u>, allowing them to make <u>lifestyle recommendations</u> to people.

If looking at what you truly love can make your heart beat faster...

...then chocolate cake must be really good for me. Unless you've been living in a cave for the past few years, you should be well aware that regular exercise is a good thing. Make sure you know how you can investigate the effect of exercise on pulse rate and recovery rate.

Q1   What is meant by the term 'recovery rate'?   [1 mark]

Treating Disease

Your body does lots of things to try and fight against diseases, but sometimes it needs a little help...

Some Medicines Just Relieve Symptoms...

1) <u>Painkillers</u> (e.g. aspirin) are drugs that relieve pain (no, really). However, they don't actually tackle the <u>cause</u> of the disease or <u>kill</u> pathogens, they just help to <u>reduce</u> the <u>symptoms</u>.

2) Other drugs do a similar kind of thing — reduce how severe the <u>symptoms</u> are or <u>how long</u> the symptoms last for, without tackling the underlying <u>cause</u>. For example, lots of "cold remedies" don't actually <u>cure</u> colds.

3) Although these drugs don't help to <u>cure</u> the disease, they can still be used to <u>ease</u> a sick person's <u>suffering</u> while their body <u>fights it off</u>.

...And Some Medicines Can Treat the Disease

1) Sometimes the body might not be able to <u>fight off</u> a disease on its <u>own</u>. In this case, it might be necessary to use <u>medicines</u> that target the <u>underlying cause</u> of a disease (rather than just helping to relieve the symptoms).

2) For example, drugs which <u>kill</u> or <u>disable</u> pathogens can be used to <u>treat</u> or <u>control diseases</u>, e.g.:

Antibiotics

1) <u>Antibiotics</u> are chemicals that kill <u>bacteria</u> without killing your own body cells. Many are produced <u>naturally</u> by <u>fungi</u> and other <u>microorganisms</u>, e.g. penicillin is made by a type of mould. Pharmaceutical companies can grow them on a <u>large scale</u> in a lab and extract the antibiotics.

2) They can also sometimes be used to <u>prevent</u> bacterial infections from happening. E.g. people in close contact with a person with <u>bacterial meningitis</u> may be given the antibiotic <u>rifampin</u>, as this stops the disease from <u>spreading</u> to them from the <u>infected person</u>.

Antivirals

1) <u>Antivirals</u> can be used to treat viral infections. They are <u>difficult</u> to produce because viruses use the <u>host cells</u> to <u>replicate</u> — it's hard to target the virus <u>without</u> damaging the cell.

2) Most antivirals don't <u>kill</u> the viruses but <u>stop</u> them from <u>reproducing</u>.

3) Some medicines can cause <u>adverse reactions</u> in a person, e.g. some people have an <u>allergic</u> reaction to <u>penicillin</u>. Some medicines can also be very <u>expensive</u>, especially if they'll need to be taken for a <u>long time</u>, and they may <u>not</u> be <u>fully effective</u>. Doctors need to <u>weigh up</u> the potential <u>benefits</u> of medicines against the <u>risks</u> and <u>costs</u> associated with them when they're deciding what to prescribe.

Overuse of Antibiotics May Make Some Diseases Difficult to Treat

1) Some bacteria are <u>naturally resistant</u> to certain antibiotics.

2) The <u>misuse</u> of antibiotics can increase the <u>rate of development</u> of these <u>resistant strains</u>. For example, if a person is prescribed a <u>course</u> of antibiotics for a <u>bacterial infection</u> and they <u>don't complete</u> the full course, resistant bacteria can become <u>more common</u>. This is because the bacteria with the <u>most resistance</u> may <u>survive the antibiotic treatment</u>. Once all the non-resistant bacteria have been killed, the resistant strains will have <u>less competition</u> and will be able to <u>grow and reproduce</u>.

3) Because of the <u>misuse</u> of antibiotics, <u>very resistant strains</u> of bacteria have developed, e.g. <u>MRSA</u> (the hospital 'superbug') is a well-known example of an antibiotic-resistant strain. The development of these very resistant strains means that the antibiotics we currently use are becoming <u>less effective</u>.

The spread of antibiotic resistant bacteria is an example of evolution by natural selection, see p.87.

4) Since superbugs like MRSA can be very <u>dangerous</u>, doctors have to balance their patient's <u>well-being</u> with the well-being of <u>other people</u> in society when they decide whether or not to prescribe antibiotics — e.g. they may not prescribe antibiotics if they're <u>not really needed</u>, such as for only <u>minor infections</u>.

GCSEs are like antibiotics — you have to finish the course...

Kapow, down with you nasty pathogens — we will kill you all. Ahem, sorry. You best learn this lot.

Q1   Explain why many antibiotics are becoming less effective as treatments for infections.   [3 marks]

Treating Cardiovascular Disease

Cardiovascular disease is a big, big problem in the UK. The good news is there are lots of ways to treat it.

Cardiovascular Disease Affects The Heart and Blood Vessels

See p.69-70 for more on the heart and blood vessels.

Cardiovascular diseases (CVD) are diseases to do with your heart and blood vessels. E.g.

1) High blood pressure and lots of LDL cholesterol can lead to the build up of fatty deposits inside arteries, narrowing them. Over time the fatty deposits harden, forming atheromas. CORONARY HEART DISEASE is when the arteries that supply the heart muscle with blood (coronary arteries) have lots of atheromas in them, which restricts blood flow to the heart.

2) Sometimes bits of atheromas can break off or damage the blood vessel, causing a blood clot. Complete blockage of an artery by atheromas or blood clots can lead to a HEART ATTACK, where part of the heart muscle is deprived of oxygen. If the blockage occurs in the brain, it can cause a STROKE.

normal artery

deposits of fat build up

thickness of artery wall unchanged

space in centre of artery shrinks, so it's harder for blood to pass through

There are Different Ways of Treating CVD

See pages 24-25 for more about risk factors for CVD.

Healthy Lifestyle

1) Making changes to your lifestyle, such as eating a healthy diet that is low in saturated fat, reducing stress, exercising regularly and quitting smoking, can reduce the risk of developing CVD in the first place — which avoids the complications of treating it after it has already developed.

2) However, even if you've already had problems, e.g. a heart attack, having a healthy lifestyle can still help. Lifestyle changes can also help other forms of treatment (see below) be more effective.

Medicines

Sometimes medicines are needed to help control the effects of CVD. For example:

1) Statins can reduce the amount of cholesterol present in the bloodstream, which can slow down the rate of fatty deposits forming. However, statins can sometimes cause serious side effects, e.g. kidney failure, liver damage and memory problems.

2) Anticoagulants are drugs which make blood clots less likely to form. However, this can cause excessive bleeding if the person is hurt.

3) Antihypertensives reduce blood pressure. This reduces the risk of atheromas and blood clots forming. Their side effects can include headaches or fainting.

Surgical Procedures

If the heart or blood vessels are too badly damaged then surgery may be needed.

1) Stents are tubes that are inserted inside arteries. They keep them open, making sure blood can pass through to the cardiac muscle, lowering the risk of heart attack. But over time, the artery can narrow again as stents can irritate the artery and make scar tissue grow.

2) If part of a blood vessel is blocked, a piece of healthy vessel taken from elsewhere can be used to bypass the blocked section. This is known as coronary bypass surgery.

3) The whole heart can be replaced with a donor heart (a heart donated after a person has died). However, the new heart does not always start pumping properly. The new heart can also be rejected because the body's immune system recognises it as 'foreign'.

fatty deposit

stent pushes artery wall out, squashing fatty deposit

more space in the centre of the artery

Heart surgery is a major procedure and, as with all surgeries, there is risk of bleeding, clots and infection.

If treatment for cardiovascular disease is needed, doctors must weigh up the likely effectiveness of each treatment against the cost and risks involved for each one, before deciding on which one to use.

Treatments can be risky and expensive, so it's much better to stop CVD from developing in the first place. The same is true for other non-communicable diseases.

Look after yerselves me hearties...

...and make sure you're aware of the drawbacks as well as the advantages for the above ways of treating CVD.

Q1 Anticoagulants make blood clots less likely. Give a disadvantage of their use in treating CVD. [1 mark]

Developing New Medicines

New medicines are constantly being <u>developed</u> and this nifty little page tells you all about how that happens.

Potential New Medicines Have to be Discovered First

1) In order to develop a new drug, a <u>target</u> that the drug will act upon needs to be <u>identified</u>.

2) The target is likely to be a <u>gene</u> or <u>protein</u> that is linked to the <u>development</u> or <u>progression</u> of the disease. E.g. the target for an <u>anti-cancer</u> drug might be an <u>enzyme</u> (a protein) that is linked to <u>tumour formation</u>.

3) Studying the <u>genomes</u> and <u>proteins</u> of plants and animals can help to <u>identify</u> targets. E.g. studying the genomes of people with and without <u>Alzheimer's disease</u> might lead to the discovery of certain gene <u>variants</u> that <u>contribute</u> to the disease. These gene variants or the proteins they code for can then be the <u>targets</u> for new Alzheimer's <u>drugs</u>. Similarly, the genomes and proteins of <u>pathogens</u> can be studied to identify targets for <u>new</u> drugs, which could help to <u>stop</u> the pathogens from <u>causing</u> disease.

4) Once a target has been <u>identified</u>, scientists then have to find a <u>chemical substance</u> that will have the <u>effect</u> they want <u>on</u> the target (e.g. <u>stop</u> an enzyme from <u>working</u>). To do this, <u>large libraries</u> of chemical substances have to be <u>screened</u> (using very <u>high-tech</u> processes) to assess their likely <u>effectiveness</u>.

5) The result of the screening is <u>unlikely</u> to find a chemical substance that will work <u>exactly</u> in the way the scientists want. Instead the <u>most promising</u> chemicals are <u>selected</u> and <u>modified</u>, and then undergo <u>further tests</u>.

Then There are Lots of Tests to Help Develop Potential Drugs

Preclinical testing:

1) In preclinical testing, drugs are <u>first</u> tested on <u>cultured human cells</u> (cultured means that they've been grown in a lab). However, you can't use human cells to test drugs that affect whole or multiple body systems, e.g. a drug for blood pressure must be tested on a whole animal.

2) The next step is to test the drug on <u>live animals</u>. <u>Both</u> of these steps are used to test that the drug <u>is effective</u> (produces the <u>effect</u> you're looking for) and to find out how <u>safe</u> it is.

Clinical testing:

1) If the drug <u>passes</u> the tests on animals then it's tested on <u>human volunteers</u> in a <u>clinical trial</u>.

2) First, the drug is tested on <u>healthy volunteers</u> to make sure that it is <u>safe</u>, i.e. that it doesn't have any <u>harmful side effects</u> when the body is working <u>normally</u>. Then, <u>successful drugs</u> can be tested on people that have the <u>disease</u>, to test its <u>effectiveness</u> and <u>safety</u>.

3) For many clinical tests, patients are <u>randomly</u> put into <u>two groups</u>. One is given the <u>new drug</u>, the other is given a <u>placebo</u>. This is to allow for the <u>placebo effect</u> (when the patient expects the treatment to work and so <u>feels better</u>, even though the treatment isn't doing anything).

> A placebo is a substance that looks like the drug being tested but doesn't do anything, e.g. a sugar pill

4) However, there are ethical issues around giving a <u>placebo</u> to people <u>with the disease</u> instead of a <u>potential treatment</u>, especially if the disease has severe symptoms (so in some trials they don't use placebos at all).

5) Clinical trials may be <u>blind</u> — the patient in the study <u>doesn't know</u> whether they're getting the <u>drug</u> or the <u>placebo</u>. In fact, they're often <u>double-blind</u> — neither the <u>patient</u> nor the <u>doctor</u> knows until all the <u>results</u> have been gathered. This is so the doctors <u>monitoring</u> the patients and <u>analysing</u> the results aren't <u>subconsciously influenced</u> by their knowledge.

6) Trials can also be <u>open-label</u> — the <u>doctor</u> and the <u>patient</u> are aware of who is receiving the <u>drug</u>. These might be used when <u>comparing</u> the effectiveness of two <u>very similar</u> drugs.

<u>All</u> new medicinal drugs have to go through testing before they can be <u>widely used</u> to <u>treat</u> patients.

The placebo effect doesn't work with revision...

Testing, retesting and then...yep, more testing. You'd know all about that anyway, it's just like being in school...

Q1 Explain how a double-blind trial would be carried out.   [2 marks]

Revision Questions for Chapter B2

Well that's <u>health and disease</u> for you — you've met some heroes and some villains, now time to learn it.

- Try these questions and <u>tick off each one</u> when you <u>get it right</u>.
- When you've done <u>all the questions</u> for a topic and are <u>completely happy</u> with it, tick off the topic.

Health and the Spread of Disease (p.13-14) ☑

1) What is a pathogen? ☑
2) What is meant by the 'incubation period' of a pathogen? ☑
3) Give an example of a disease that is spread through the air. ☑

Defence Against Pathogens and the Immune System (p.15-16) ☑

4) Describe how the skin acts as a defence against pathogens. ☑
5) What are platelets? ☑
6) Give an example of a chemical defence against pathogens found in humans. ☑
7) How do white blood cells recognise specific pathogens? ☑

Reducing and Preventing the Spread of Disease (p.17-18) ☑

8) Explain why isolating infected individuals can help to prevent the spread of disease. ☑
9) Give one method for preventing the transmission of HIV. ☑
10) Give one benefit and one cost of using biological control to prevent the spread of a disease in a crop. ☑
11) Give one potential risk of using vaccinations as a way of protecting people from diseases. ☑

Detecting Diseases and Culturing Microorganisms (p.19-21) ☑

12) Describe one way in which plant pathologists might identify a plant disease in the field. ☑
13) Explain how a plant disease may be identified using isolation and reinfection. ☑
14) There are ways in which you can make sure an experiment testing the effect of antibiotics on bacteria does not become contaminated. Give three of these ways. ☑

Monoclonal Antibodies (p.22-23) ☐

15) How can you use monoclonal antibodies to detect a particular pathogen? ☑
16) How can monoclonal antibodies be used to trigger an immune response against cancer cells? ☑

Non-Communicable Diseases (p.24-25) ☑

17) What is meant by a risk factor for a non-communicable disease? ☑
18) Apart from lifestyle factors, give an example of a risk factor that might be associated with a non-communicable disease. ☑
19) Give one non-communicable disease which may be associated with smoking. ☑

Interpreting Data on Disease and Investigating Pulse Rate (p.26-27) ☑

20) What is meant by a positive correlation? ☑
21) Briefly describe how you could investigate the effect of exercise on pulse rate. ☑

Treating Disease (p.28-30) ☑

22) What do antiviral drugs do? ☑
23) Give an example of a surgical procedure which can help to treat cardiovascular disease. ☑
24) How can genome sequences help in the discovery of new drugs. ☑

Enzymes

Chemical reactions are what make you work. And enzymes are what make them work.

Enzymes Are Catalysts Produced by Living Things

> A catalyst is a substance which increases the speed of a reaction, without being changed or used up in the reaction.

1) Living things have thousands of different chemical reactions going on inside them all the time.

2) These reactions need to be carefully controlled — to get the right amounts of substances.

3) You can usually make a reaction happen more quickly by raising the temperature. This would speed up the useful reactions but also the unwanted ones too... not good.

4) So... living things produce enzymes which act as biological catalysts. Enzymes reduce the need for high temperatures and we only have enzymes to speed up the useful chemical reactions in the body.

5) Enzymes catalyse reactions in both animals and plants — including photosynthesis in plants (see p.34).

Enzymes Have Special Shapes So They Can Catalyse Reactions

1) Chemical reactions usually involve things either being split apart or joined together.

2) The substrate is the molecule changed in the reaction.

3) Every enzyme has an active site — the part where it joins on to its substrate to catalyse the reaction.

4) Enzymes usually only work with one substrate. They are said to have a high specificity for their substrate.

5) This is because, for the enzyme to work, the substrate has to fit into the active site. If the substrate's shape doesn't match the active site's shape, then the reaction won't be catalysed. This is called the 'lock and key' model, because the substrate fits into the enzyme just like a key fits into a lock.

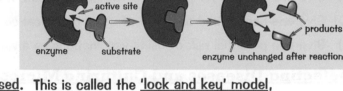

enzyme-substrate complex · active site · products · enzyme · substrate · enzyme unchanged after reaction

Temperature, pH and Substrate Concentration Affect the Rate of Reaction

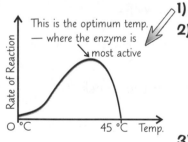

This is the optimum temp. — where the enzyme is most active

Rate of Reaction — 0 °C — 45 °C — Temp.

1) Changing the temperature changes the rate of an enzyme-catalysed reaction.

2) Like with any reaction, a higher temperature increases the rate at first. The enzymes and substrate have more energy, so they move about more and are more likely to collide and form enzyme-substrate complexes. But if it gets too hot, some of the bonds holding the enzyme together break. This changes the shape of the enzyme's active site, so the substrate won't fit any more. The enzyme is said to be denatured.

3) All enzymes have an optimum temperature that they work best at.

4) The pH also affects enzymes. If it's too high or too low, the pH interferes with the bonds holding the enzyme together. This changes the shape of the active site and denatures the enzyme.

Optimum pH — Rate of Reaction — pH

5) All enzymes have an optimum pH that they work best at. It's often neutral pH 7, but not always.

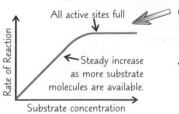

All active sites full

Steady increase as more substrate molecules are available.

Rate of Reaction — Substrate concentration

6) Substrate concentration also affects the rate of reaction — the higher the substrate concentration, the faster the reaction. This is because it's more likely that the enzyme will meet up and react with a substrate molecule.

7) This is only true up to a point though. After that, there are so many substrate molecules that the enzymes have about as much as they can cope with (all the active sites are full), and adding more makes no difference.

If the lock and key mechanism fails, get in through a window...

Make sure you use the special terms like 'active site' and 'denatured' — the examiners will love it.

Q1   Explain why enzymes have an optimum pH.   [3 marks]

More on Enzymes

You'll soon know how to investigate the effect of a <u>variable</u> on the rate of <u>enzyme activity</u>... I bet you're thrilled.

You Can Investigate How Temperature Affects Enzyme Activity

There are a couple of <u>different ways</u> to investigate how <u>temperature</u> affects <u>enzyme activity</u>. You can also <u>adapt</u> these experiments to measure variables <u>other than temperature</u>. For example:

1) To investigate the effect of <u>pH</u>, add a <u>buffer solution</u> with a different <u>pH level</u> to different tubes containing the enzyme-substrate mixture.

A buffer solution is able to resist changes in pH.

2) Vary the initial <u>concentration</u> of the <u>substrate</u> to investigate the effect of <u>substrate concentration</u>.

3) Vary the initial <u>concentration</u> of the <u>enzyme</u> to investigate the effect of <u>enzyme concentration</u>.

You Can Measure How Fast a Product Appears...

1) The enzyme <u>catalase</u> catalyses the <u>breakdown</u> of <u>hydrogen peroxide</u> into <u>water</u> and <u>oxygen</u>.

2) You can collect the <u>oxygen</u> and measure <u>how much</u> is produced in a <u>set time</u>.

3) Use a <u>pipette</u> to add a set amount of <u>hydrogen peroxide</u> to a <u>boiling tube</u>. Put the tube in a <u>water bath</u> at 10 °C and <u>wait</u> about five minutes.

4) Then <u>set up</u> the rest of the apparatus as shown. Add a source of <u>catalase</u> (e.g. a cube of potato) to the <u>hydrogen peroxide</u> and quickly <u>attach the bung</u>.
(Keep the boiling tube in the water bath.)

5) Record how much <u>oxygen</u> is produced in the <u>first minute</u>.

6) <u>Repeat</u> steps 3-5 <u>three times</u> and calculate the <u>mean</u>. Then repeat the <u>whole experiment</u> with the water bath at 20 °C, 30 °C and 40 °C.

7) <u>Control any variables</u> (e.g. pH, the potato used, the size of potato pieces, etc.) to make it a <u>fair test</u>.

8) After the experiment you can calculate the <u>mean rate of reaction</u> at each temperature to analyse your results. <u>Rate</u> is a measure of how much something <u>changes over time</u>. To calculate a rate you need to <u>divide</u> the <u>amount that something has changed</u> by the <u>time taken for the change to happen</u>. So for this experiment, you calculate the mean rate of reaction by <u>dividing</u> the mean <u>volume of oxygen</u> produced in cm³ (this is the <u>change</u>) by the <u>time taken</u> (i.e. 60 s). The units will be cm³/second.

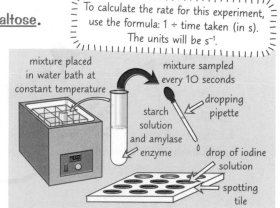

water bath at constant temperature — measuring cylinder — delivery tube — amount of oxygen produced per minute is measured — source of catalase (e.g. potato) — hydrogen peroxide solution

There's more on variables and fair tests on p.100.

...Or How Fast a Substrate Disappears

1) The enzyme <u>amylase</u> catalyses the breakdown of <u>starch</u> to <u>maltose</u>.

2) It's easy to <u>detect starch</u> using <u>iodine solution</u> — if starch is present, the iodine solution will change from <u>browny-orange</u> to <u>blue-black</u>.

3) <u>Set up</u> the apparatus as in the diagram. Put a drop of iodine solution into <u>each well</u> on the spotting tile. Use <u>continuous sampling</u> to record <u>how long</u> it takes for the amylase to <u>break down</u> all of the starch. To do this, take a <u>fresh sample</u> of the mixture every ten seconds and put a drop into a new well. Once the iodine solution <u>does not</u> turn blue-black, it means all the starch has been <u>converted</u> to maltose.

4) <u>Repeat</u> with the water bath at <u>different temperatures</u> to see how it <u>affects</u> the time taken for the starch to be broken down. Remember to <u>control</u> all of the <u>variables</u> each time.

To calculate the rate for this experiment, use the formula: 1 ÷ time taken (in s). The units will be s⁻¹.

mixture placed in water bath at constant temperature — mixture sampled every 10 seconds — dropping pipette — starch solution and amylase enzyme — drop of iodine solution — spotting tile

If only enzymes could speed up revision...

The key thing with experiments is to only change the thing you're testing — and absolutely nothing else. Sorted.

Q1 An enzyme-controlled reaction was carried out at 25 °C. After 60 seconds, 33 cm³ of product had been released. Calculate the rate of reaction in cm³/s.

[1 mark]

Photosynthesis

You don't know <u>photosynthesis</u> 'til you know its <u>equation</u>. It's in a nice <u>green box</u> so you can't possibly miss it.

Plants are Able to Make Their Own Food by Photosynthesis

1) During photosynthesis, <u>photosynthetic organisms</u>, such as <u>green plants</u> and <u>algae</u>, use <u>energy</u> from the Sun to make <u>glucose</u>.

Some prokaryotes can also photosynthesise, although they don't have chloroplasts (see below)

2) Some of the glucose is used during cellular <u>respiration</u> (see page 57) and some is converted to <u>starch</u> and <u>stored</u>. Some glucose is also used to make <u>larger</u>, <u>complex molecules</u> that the plants or algae need to <u>grow</u>, e.g. <u>lipids</u>, <u>proteins</u>, and <u>carbohydrates</u> besides starch. These make up the organism's <u>biomass</u>.

3) Photosynthesis happens inside subcellular structures called <u>chloroplasts</u> (see page 2). These contain the <u>enzymes</u> that <u>catalyse</u> reactions in photosynthesis, as well as <u>chlorophyll</u>, which <u>absorbs light</u>. Energy is <u>transferred</u> to the <u>chlorophyll</u> from the environment by <u>light</u>. This is the <u>equation</u> for photosynthesis:

$$\text{carbon dioxide} + \text{water} \xrightarrow[\text{chlorophyll}]{\text{LIGHT}} \text{glucose} + \text{oxygen}$$
$$6CO_2 + 6H_2O \xrightarrow[\text{chlorophyll}]{\text{LIGHT}} C_6H_{12}O_6 + 6O_2$$

4) Photosynthesis is <u>endothermic</u> — <u>energy</u> is transferred from the <u>environment</u> during photosynthesis.

5) <u>Lots</u> of <u>chemical reactions</u> happen during photosynthesis, but it takes place in <u>two main stages</u>. First, energy transferred by <u>light</u> to the chlorophyll is used to split <u>water</u> into <u>oxygen gas</u> and <u>hydrogen ions</u> — the oxygen is released as a <u>waste product</u>.

6) <u>Carbon dioxide gas</u> then combines with the <u>hydrogen ions</u> to make <u>glucose</u>.

The Starch Test Shows Whether Photosynthesis is Taking Place | PRACTICAL

Remember, <u>glucose</u> is <u>stored</u> by plants as <u>starch</u>. If a plant can't <u>photosynthesise</u>, it can't make <u>starch</u> — you can use this to show that <u>light</u> and <u>CO$_2$</u> are needed for photosynthesis.

First, you need to know how to <u>test a leaf</u> for starch. Start by dunking the leaf in <u>boiling water</u> (hold it with tweezers or forceps). This <u>stops</u> any <u>chemical reactions</u> happening inside the leaf. Now put the leaf in a boiling tube with some <u>ethanol</u> and heat it gently in an electric water bath — this gets rid of any <u>chlorophyll</u> and makes the leaf a <u>white-ish</u> colour. Finally, <u>rinse</u> the leaf in <u>cold water</u> and add a few drops of <u>iodine solution</u> — if <u>starch</u> is <u>present</u> the leaf will turn <u>blue-black</u>. Now for the experiments themselves...

Ethanol is highly flammable — keep it away from naked flames, e.g. Bunsen burners.

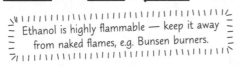

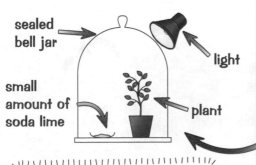

sealed bell jar

light

small amount of soda lime

plant

For both of these tests, it's important that any variables that could affect the results, e.g. the temperature, are controlled.

1) Start by <u>destarching</u> some plants (i.e. leave them in the dark for 48 hours so they use up their starch stores).

2) To show that <u>light</u> is <u>required</u> for <u>photosynthesis</u>, keep one plant <u>in the dark</u> and move the other one <u>into the light</u> for a while — then perform the <u>starch test</u> on a leaf from each plant. The leaf from the plant moved to the <u>light</u> should turn <u>blue-black</u>, but the leaf from the plant kept in the dark <u>won't</u>. This shows that <u>light is needed</u> for photosynthesis, as no starch has been made in the leaf grown without light.

3) A similar investigation can be conducted (using the apparatus shown on the left) to show that <u>CO$_2$</u> is needed for <u>photosynthesis</u>. Soda lime <u>absorbs CO$_2$</u> out of the air — so if you leave a plant in the jar for a while and then <u>test</u> a leaf for starch, it <u>won't</u> turn <u>blue-black</u>. This shows that <u>no starch</u> has been made in the leaf, which means that <u>CO$_2$ is needed</u> for photosynthesis to happen.

I'm working on sunshine — woah oh...

You must learn the photosynthesis equation. Learn it so well that you'll still remember it when you're 109.

Q1   Explain how the starch test can be used to show that plants need light to photosynthesise.   [4 marks]

Investigating the Rate of Photosynthesis

If you've always wanted to investigate how <u>different factors</u> affect the <u>rate</u> of photosynthesis, you're in luck...

Oxygen Production Shows the Rate of Photosynthesis | PRACTICAL

1) The rate of photosynthesis can be affected by <u>light intensity</u>, <u>concentration of CO_2</u> and <u>temperature</u>. Any of these can become <u>limiting factors</u>, meaning they can stop photosynthesis from happening any <u>faster</u>.

2) You can <u>investigate</u> how each of the different factors affect the <u>rate of photosynthesis</u>. A classic way to do this is to use <u>pondweed</u> and to measure <u>oxygen production</u> over <u>time</u>.

3) The rate at which the pondweed produces <u>oxygen</u> corresponds to the rate at which it's photosynthesising — the <u>faster</u> the rate of oxygen production, the <u>faster</u> the rate of photosynthesis.

4) The box below describes the <u>basic method</u> you could use — the ways in which you could alter the experiment to test the different factors are shown on the next page.

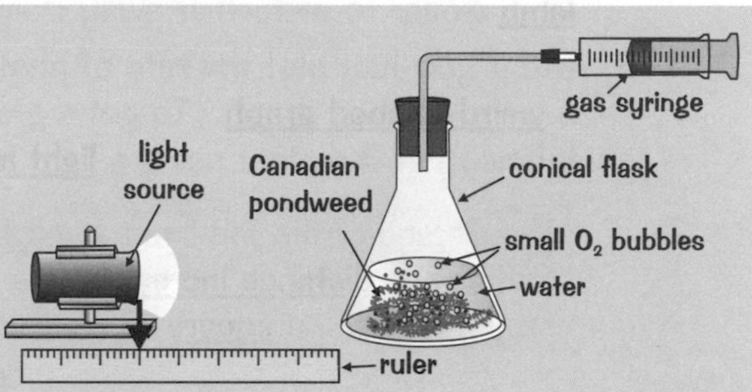

---

1) The <u>apparatus</u> is <u>set up</u> according to the <u>diagram</u>. This gas syringe should be empty to start with.

2) A set amount of <u>sodium hydrogencarbonate</u> (which gives off CO_2) may be added to the water in the conical flask to <u>control</u> the amount of CO_2 the pondweed receives. You could also use a <u>heat shield</u> (e.g. a beaker of water) to stop the heat from the lamp affecting the results. Put the conical flask <u>in the beaker of water</u> or put the beaker <u>between</u> the <u>flask and the lamp</u>.

3) The pondweed is left to photosynthesise for a <u>set amount of time</u>.

4) As it photosynthesises, the oyxgen released will collect in the <u>gas syringe</u>. This allows you to <u>accurately measure</u> the <u>volume</u> of oxygen produced.

5) The results are recorded in a table, and the experiment is then <u>repeated</u> to test a <u>range</u> of values for the <u>factor being investigated</u>, e.g. a range of different distances from the light source.

6) Variables other than the one being investigated should be kept the <u>same</u>, e.g. the other limiting factors, the time the pondweed is left for.

light source — *Canadian pondweed* — *gas syringe* — *conical flask* — *small O_2 bubbles* — *water* — *ruler*

You could also measure how much oxygen is being produced by counting the bubbles, but it's not as accurate (see p.113).

You Can Calculate Rate from a Graph

Once you've written your results in a table, you can <u>plot</u> them in a <u>graph</u>. (There's more on plotting graphs on p.103.) Graphs aren't just nice to look at — they're useful for spotting patterns in your results. You can carry out <u>calculations</u> from them too. If you want to calculate the rate of photosynthesis from a graph of your results, <u>volume of oxygen</u> should go on the <u>y-axis</u> and <u>time</u> should go on the <u>x-axis</u>.

EXAMPLE: The graph below shows the first six hours of photosynthesis by a plant. Calculate the mean rate of photosynthesis during this six hour period, giving your answer in cm³/hour.

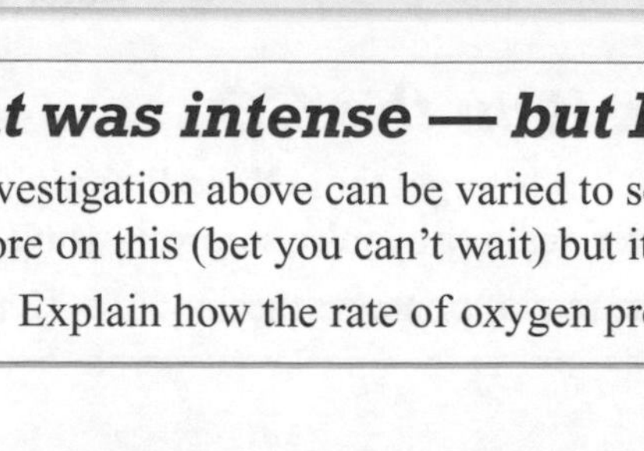

Mean volume of oxygen produced (cm³) vs *Time (h)*

1) <u>Read off</u> the <u>volume of oxygen</u> produced after <u>6 hours</u>.   3 cm³

2) <u>Divide</u> the <u>volume</u> by the <u>time taken</u> to produce it.   3/6 = 0.5

3) <u>Write</u> your answer with the <u>correct units</u>.   0.5 cm³/hour

---

That was intense — but I see light at the end of the tunnel...

The investigation above can be varied to see how different factors affect the rate of photosynthesis. The next page has more on this (bet you can't wait) but it's best to understand what's happening here before moving on.

Q1   Explain how the rate of oxygen production corresponds to the rate of photosynthesis.   [2 marks]

Limiting Factors of Photosynthesis

Before you start on this page, make sure you've read the <u>photosynthesis experiment</u> from the last page. OK...

Here Are Three Important Graphs for Rate of Photosynthesis

Not Enough LIGHT Slows Down the Rate of Photosynthesis

1) Light transfers the <u>energy</u> needed for photosynthesis.

2) As the <u>light level</u> is raised, the rate of photosynthesis <u>increases steadily</u> — but only up to a <u>certain point</u>.

3) Beyond that, it <u>won't</u> make any difference — it'll be either the <u>temperature</u> or the <u>CO_2 level</u> which is the limiting factor.

4) In the lab you can investigate light intensity by <u>moving</u> a <u>lamp</u> closer to or further away from your plant.

5) But if you just plot the rate of photosynthesis against "distance of lamp from the plant", you get a <u>weird-shaped graph</u>. To get a graph like the one above you either need to <u>measure</u> the light intensity at the plant using a <u>light meter</u> or do a bit of nifty maths with your results. Here's why:

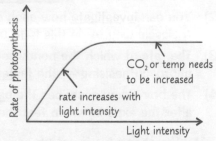

The distance from the lamp and light intensity are <u>inversely proportional</u> to each other — this means that as the <u>distance increases</u>, the <u>light intensity decreases</u>. However, light intensity decreases in proportion to the <u>square</u> of the distance. This is called the <u>inverse square law</u> and is written like this:

Putting one over the distance shows the <u>inverse</u>.

$$\text{light intensity (i)} \propto \frac{1}{\text{distance (d)}^2}$$

<u>Halving</u> the distance → intensity is $2 \times 2 = \underline{4}$ times <u>greater</u>
<u>Tripling</u> the distance → intensity is $3 \times 3 = \underline{9}$ times <u>smaller</u>

Too Little CARBON DIOXIDE Also Slows it Down

1) CO_2 is one of the <u>substrates</u> needed for photosynthesis.

2) This means that <u>increasing the concentration</u> of <u>CO_2</u> will increase the rate of photosynthesis — but only up to a point. After this the graph <u>flattens out</u> — CO_2 is no longer the <u>limiting factor</u>.

3) If <u>CO_2</u> is in plentiful supply, then the factor limiting photosynthesis must be <u>light</u> or <u>temperature</u>.

4) In the experiment on the previous page, dissolving different amounts of <u>sodium hydrogencarbonate</u> in the same volume of water will vary the CO_2 concentration.

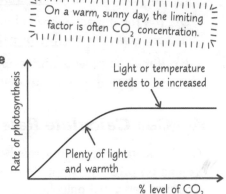

On a warm, sunny day, the limiting factor is often CO_2 concentration.

The TEMPERATURE has to be Just Right

1) Usually, if the temperature is the <u>limiting factor</u> it's because it's <u>too low</u> — the <u>enzymes</u> needed for photosynthesis work more <u>slowly</u> at low temperatures.

2) But if the plant gets <u>too hot</u>, the enzymes it needs for photosynthesis and its other reactions will be <u>denatured</u> — the <u>rate</u> of reaction <u>decreases</u> dramatically.

3) This happens at about <u>45 °C</u> (pretty hot for outdoors, but <u>greenhouses</u> can get that hot if you're not careful).

4) Experimentally, you can <u>vary</u> the <u>temperature</u> of the conical flask (see p.35), using a <u>water bath</u>.

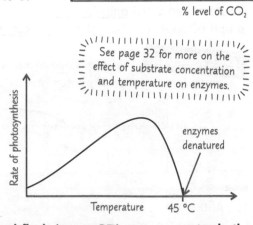

See page 32 for more on the effect of substrate concentration and temperature on enzymes.

Don't blame it on the sunshine, don't blame it on the CO_2...

...don't blame it on the temperature, blame it on the plant. And now you'll never forget these three limiting factors. in photosynthesis. No... well, make sure you read these pages over and over again 'til you're sure you won't.

Q1   Describe the relationship between increasing light intensity and the rate of photosynthesis.   **[2 marks]**

Diffusion, Osmosis and Active Transport

Substances can move in and out of cells by diffusion, osmosis and active transport...

Diffusion — Don't be Put Off by the Fancy Word

1) Diffusion is simple. It's just the gradual movement of particles from places where there are lots of them to places where there are fewer of them. That's all it is — just the natural tendency for stuff to spread out. Here's the fancy definition:

> DIFFUSION is the net (overall) movement of particles from an area of higher concentration to an area of lower concentration.

If something moves from an area of higher concentration to an area of lower concentration it is said to have moved down a concentration gradient.

2) Diffusion happens in both liquids and gases — that's because the particles in these substances are free to move about randomly.

3) Diffusion continues until the concentration of the diffusing particles is even in both areas. This is what's happening when the smell of perfume diffuses through the air in a room:

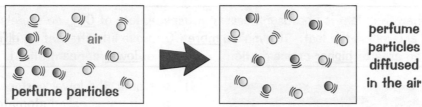

perfume particles diffused in the air

4) Cell membranes are partially permeable. This means that only very small molecules can move through them — things like glucose, amino acids, water and oxygen. Big molecules like starch, sucrose and proteins can't fit through the membrane.

Osmosis is a Special Case of Diffusion, That's All

> OSMOSIS is the net movement of water molecules across a partially permeable membrane from a region of higher water concentration to a region of lower water concentration.

1) The water molecules actually pass both ways through the membrane during osmosis. This happens because water molecules move about randomly all the time.

2) But because there are more water molecules on one side than on the other, there's a steady net flow of water into the region with fewer water molecules, i.e. into the stronger sugar solution.

3) This means the strong sugar solution gets more dilute. The water acts like it's trying to "even up" the concentration either side of the membrane.

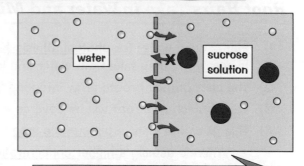

Net movement of water molecules

Active Transport Works Against a Concentration Gradient

> ACTIVE TRANSPORT is the movement of particles across a membrane against a concentration gradient (i.e. from an area of lower to an area of higher concentration) using energy transferred during respiration.

1) Active transport is a bit different from diffusion because particles are moved up a concentration gradient rather than down. The process also requires energy (unlike diffusion, which is a passive process).

2) There's an example of active transport at work on the next page.

Revision by diffusion — you wish...

Hopefully there'll have been a net movement of information from this page into your brain...

Q1   Give two differences between the processes of diffusion and active transport.   [2 marks]

Transport in Plants and Prokaryotes

Diffusion, osmosis and active transport are at work in all living organisms, including plants and prokaryotes. These pages illustrate how they aid transport — if you're unsure about them, look back at the previous page.

Exchanging Substances is Trickier in Multicellular Organisms

1) Single-celled organisms, including prokaryotes (see p.2), are only one cell big — therefore substances can diffuse straight into and out of them across their partially permeable cell membranes.

2) In multicellular organisms, such as animals and plants, diffusion across the outer surface is more difficult because some cells are deep inside the organism — it's a long way from them to the outside environment and so specialised exchange surfaces are needed.

CO_2 and O_2 move through Stomata and Cell Membranes in Plants

When plants photosynthesise they use up CO_2 from the atmosphere and produce oxygen as a waste product. These gases move in and out of plants and their cells by diffusion.

> E.g. when the plant is photosynthesising it uses up lots of CO_2, so there's hardly any inside the leaf. This makes more CO_2 move into the leaf by diffusion (from an area of higher concentration to an area of lower concentration).

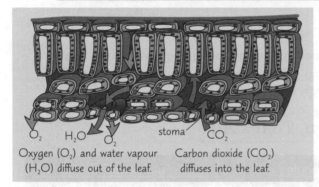

Oxygen (O_2) and water vapour (H_2O) diffuse out of the leaf.

Carbon dioxide (CO_2) diffuses into the leaf.

1) In plants, the lower surface of a leaf is full of tiny pores called stomata (see p.41).

2) The stomata are there to let gases like CO_2 and O_2 diffuse in and out. They also allow water vapour to escape — which is known as transpiration (see p.40).

3) These gases diffuse between air spaces inside the leaf and the plant's cells through the cells' partially permeable outer membrane.

Root Hairs Take in Water and Mineral Ions

> Molecules can only cross a membrane when they're right next to it, so a large surface area means loads more molecules are close to the membrane.

1) Plants need water for photosynthesis (amongst other things) and mineral ions for growth. They take both water and ions in through their roots.

2) The cells on plant roots grow into long 'hairs' which stick out into the soil.

3) Each branch of a root will be covered in millions of these microscopic hairs.

4) This gives the plant a big surface area for absorbing water and mineral ions from the soil:

- There's usually a higher concentration of water in the soil than there is inside the plant, so the water is drawn into the root hair cell across the partially permeable cell membrane by osmosis.

- Plants need nitrogen to make proteins. They get nitrogen from nitrate ions (NO_3^-). These mineral ions move into root cells by active transport, since the concentration of mineral ions in the root hair cells is usually higher than in the soil. The cells use molecules of ATP (see p.57) to provide energy to actively transport the ions through the cell membrane.

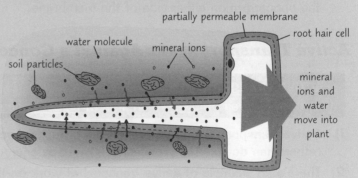

soil particles

water molecule

mineral ions

partially permeable membrane

root hair cell

mineral ions and water move into plant

Active transport — get on yer bike...

All cell membranes are partially permeable — this allows control over what goes in and out of the cell.

Q1   How are plant roots adapted to be able to absorb lots of water and mineral ions from the soil?   [2 marks]

Investigating Diffusion and Osmosis

For all you non-believers — here are a few experiments you can do to see diffusion and osmosis in action.

You Can Investigate Diffusion in a Non-Living System | PRACTICAL

Phenolphthalein is a pH indicator — it's pink in alkaline solutions and colourless in acidic solutions. You can use it to investigate diffusion in agar jelly:

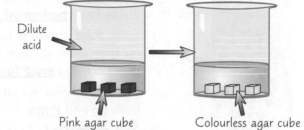

Pink agar cube   Colourless agar cube

1) First, you need some agar jelly made up with phenolphthalein and dilute sodium hydroxide. Dilute sodium hydroxide is an alkali, so the jelly should be a lovely shade of pink.

2) Now add some dilute hydrochloric acid to a beaker. Measure out and cut some cubes from the jelly — then put them in the beaker of acid.

3) If the cubes are left they'll eventually turn colourless as the acid diffuses into the agar jelly and neutralises the sodium hydroxide — use a stopwatch to time how long it takes.

4) You could investigate how varying the concentration of the acid (e.g. between 0.1 and 1 M) affects the rate of diffusion. Keep everything apart from the concentration of acid the same.

You can Observe the Effect of Sugar Solutions on Plant Tissue | PRACTICAL

There's a fairly dull experiment you can do to show osmosis at work.

1) You cut up an innocent potato into identical cylinders, and get some beakers with different sugar solutions in them. One should be pure water and another should be a very concentrated sugar solution (e.g. 1 mol/dm³). Then you can have a few others with concentrations in between (e.g. 0.2 mol/dm³, 0.4 mol/dm³, 0.6 mol/dm³, etc.)

Pure water → ← Potato cylinders → ← Conc. sugar solution

2) You measure the mass of each cylinder, then leave one cylinder in each beaker for 24 hours or so. (Alternatively, you could measure the length of each cylinder.)

3) After taking the cylinders out, dry them with a paper towel and measure their masses again.

4) The only thing that you should change in this experiment is the concentration of the sucrose solution. Everything else (e.g. the volume of solution, the time the cylinders are left for, the temperature, etc.) must be kept the same or your results won't be valid (see p.100).

5) Once you've got your results you can calculate the percentage change in mass for the cylinders in each beaker, plot a graph and analyse your results.

> By calculating the percentage change (see p.42), you can compare the effect of sugar concentration on cylinders that didn't have the same initial mass.

At the points above the x-axis, the water concentration of the sucrose solutions is higher than in the cylinders. The cylinders gain mass as water is drawn in by osmosis.

Concentration of sucrose solution (M)

% change in mass

Where there is no change in mass (where the curve crosses the x-axis) the fluid inside the cylinders and the sucrose solution have the same water concentration.

At the points below the x-axis, the water concentration of the sucrose solutions is lower than in the cylinders. This causes the cylinders to lose water so their mass decreases.

6) Carrying out repeats and calculating the mean percentage change in mass will reduce the effect of random errors on your experiment (see page 102).

So that's how they make skinny fries...

The experiment above used sucrose as a solute, but you could do the experiment with different solutes (e.g. salt).

Q1   Potato cylinders in a salt solution with a concentration of 0.3 mol/dm³ do not change mass. What does this tell you about the concentration of the solution in the potato cells? Explain your answer.   **[3 marks]**

Xylem and Phloem

Instead of blood vessels, plants have <u>two</u> types of transport vessel (<u>xylem</u> and <u>phloem</u>) for transporting stuff around. <u>Both</u> types of vessel go to <u>every part</u> of the plant in a <u>continuous system</u>, but they're totally <u>separate</u>.

Phloem Tubes Transport Food Substances

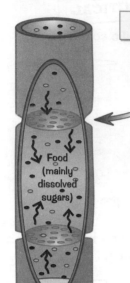

1) <u>Phloem tubes</u> are made of <u>columns</u> of <u>living cells</u> called <u>sieve tube elements</u>. These have <u>perforated end-plates</u> to allow stuff to flow through.

2) Sieve tube elements have <u>no nucleus</u>. This means that they <u>can't survive</u> on their own, so each sieve tube element has a <u>companion cell</u>. These cells carry out the <u>living functions</u> for both themselves and their sieve cells.

3) Phloem vessels transport <u>food substances</u> (mainly <u>sugars</u>) both <u>up</u> and <u>down</u> the stem to growing and storage tissues.

4) This <u>movement</u> of food substances around the plant is known as <u>translocation</u>. Sugars are usually <u>translocated</u> from <u>photosynthetic tissues</u>, e.g. the leaves, to <u>non-photosynthetic tissues</u>, e.g. the roots.

5) The <u>sugars</u> enter the phloem by <u>active transport</u>. They are then pushed around by <u>water</u>, which enters the phloem by <u>osmosis</u>.

Xylem Tubes Take Water and Ions UP

1) <u>Xylem tubes</u> are made of <u>dead cells</u> joined end to end with <u>no</u> connecting cell walls between them (to create a long tube) and a hole (<u>lumen</u>) down the middle.

2) The <u>thick side walls</u> are made of <u>cellulose</u>. They're <u>strong</u> and <u>stiff</u>, which gives the plant <u>support</u>. The cell walls are also strengthened with a material called <u>lignin</u>.

3) Xylem tubes carry <u>water</u> and <u>mineral ions</u> (e.g. nitrates) in <u>aqueous solution</u> from the roots <u>up the stem</u> to the leaves in the <u>transpiration stream</u> (see below).

Aqueous solution just means the ions are dissolved in the water.

Transpiration is the Loss of Water from the Plant

1) Transpiration is caused by the <u>evaporation</u> and <u>diffusion</u> of water from a plant's surface. Most transpiration happens at the <u>leaves</u>.

2) This evaporation and diffusion creates a slight <u>shortage</u> of water in the leaf, and so more water is drawn up from the rest of the plant through the <u>xylem vessels</u> to replace it.

3) This in turn means more water is drawn up from the <u>roots</u>, and so there's a constant <u>transpiration stream</u> of water through the plant.

Head back to page 38 to see how root hair cells are adapted for taking up water.

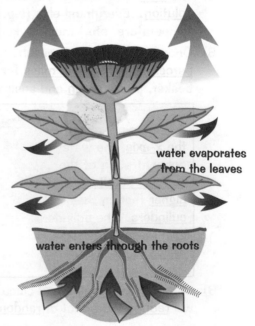

water evaporates from the leaves

water enters through the roots

Transpiration is just a <u>side-effect</u> of the way leaves are adapted for <u>photosynthesis</u>. They have to have <u>stomata</u> in them so that gases can be exchanged easily (see page 38). Because there's <u>more water inside</u> the plant than in the <u>air outside</u>, the water escapes   m the leaves through the stomata by diffusion.

Don't let revision stress you out — just go with the phloem...

Phloem goes up and down, whereas xylem just goes up. You could remember it as xy to the sky... it sort of rhymes.

Q1   Explain why there is a continuous upward flow of water in plants.   [3 marks]

Stomata

You've not learnt about <u>transpiration</u> 'til you've learnt about stomata (sadly)...

Stomata Open and Close Automatically

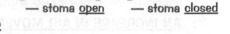

It's one stoma, but two or more stomata.

You should remember from p.38 that stomata are <u>tiny pores</u> on the surface of a plant, which allow <u>CO_2</u> and <u>oxygen</u> to <u>diffuse</u> directly in and out of a leaf. They also allow <u>water vapour</u> to escape during transpiration (see previous page). Stomata are able to open and close to control the amount of water lost from the leaves.

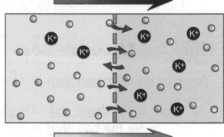

guard cells
stoma

guard cells turgid
— stoma <u>open</u>

guard cells flaccid
— stoma <u>closed</u>

1) Stomata are surrounded by <u>guard cells</u>, which <u>change shape</u> to control the size of the pore.

2) When the guard cells are <u>turgid</u> (swollen with water) the stomata are <u>open</u>, and when the guard cells are <u>flaccid</u> (low on water and limp) the stomata are <u>closed</u>.

3) <u>Stomata</u> close <u>automatically</u> when supplies of water start to <u>dry up</u> — they're also <u>sensitive to light</u> and <u>close at night</u> to <u>save water</u> without losing out on photosynthesis.

4) <u>Changes</u> in the <u>concentration of ions</u> inside the guard cells help to open and close the stomata:

- In response to stimuli like <u>light</u>, <u>potassium ions</u> (K^+) are pumped <u>into guard cells</u>.

- This <u>increases</u> the <u>solute concentration</u> of the guard cells, which <u>decreases</u> the concentration of <u>water molecules</u>.

- <u>Water</u> then moves <u>into</u> the guard cells by <u>osmosis</u>. This makes the guard cells <u>turgid</u> and the stoma <u>opens</u>.

- When potassium ions <u>leave</u> the guard cells, the <u>concentration of water molecules</u> in the cell <u>increases</u>.

- <u>Water</u> then moves <u>out</u> by <u>osmosis</u>, the guard cells become <u>flaccid</u> and the stoma <u>closes</u>.

K^+ pumped across guard cell membrane

Movement of water into guard cell by osmosis

5) If the plant's really short of water, the <u>cytoplasm</u> inside its cells starts to <u>shrink</u> and the membrane <u>pulls away</u> from the cell wall. A cell in this condition is said to be <u>plasmolysed</u>.

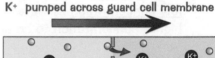

You Can View Stomata, Xylem and Phloem Under a Microscope

<u>Stomata</u> can be observed using a <u>light microscope</u>. You can prepare a <u>slide</u> to view them on using the following (ridiculously easy) method:

PRACTICAL

1) Paint two thin layers of <u>clear nail varnish</u> onto the leaf you want to look at. Leave the varnish to <u>dry</u> in between each coat.

2) Put a piece of <u>clear sticky tape</u> over the top of the painted leaf and use it to <u>peel</u> the varnish <u>off</u> slowly. The varnish will have an <u>impression</u> of the leaf's <u>surface</u>.

3) <u>Stick</u> the tape with the varnish onto a <u>microscope slide</u>.

You can then <u>view</u> your slide under the microscope (see p.3 for how to do this). You should be able to <u>count</u> the <u>stomata</u> and <u>guard cells</u> from the impression on the varnish. If you <u>compare</u> the top and bottom surfaces of a leaf you should find that there are <u>more stomata</u> on the <u>bottom</u> of the leaf.

You can also use a light microscope to observe the <u>structure</u> of <u>xylem</u> and <u>phloem</u> in <u>thin sections</u> of a plant's stem. If stem is left upright in a beaker of <u>eosin dye</u>, the dye will travel up the stem, staining the <u>xylem</u> red. A thin section of the stem can then be taken and viewed on a slide under a microscope.

See p.3 for how to prepare a slide.

I say stomaaarta, you say stomaaayta...

A tree can lose around 1000 litres of water from its leaves every day. That's about as much water as the average person drinks in a year. No wonder the stomata close when the soil's dry or it's too dark to photosynthesise.

Q1   Explain how the stomata open in response to light.   [4 marks]

Transpiration Rate

If you thought that stuff on <u>transpiration</u> was <u>interesting</u>, you're in luck — here's another page all about it...

Transpiration Rate is Affected by Three Main Things

1) <u>AN INCREASE IN LIGHT INTENSITY</u> — the <u>brighter</u> the light, the <u>greater</u> the transpiration rate. Bright light <u>increases</u> the rate of <u>photosynthesis</u>. This increases the <u>demand for water</u> in the <u>leaves</u>, so more is drawn up from the roots. Bright light also causes the <u>stomata</u> to <u>open</u> to let CO_2 in, allowing more water vapour to diffuse out. <u>Stomata</u> begin to <u>close</u> as it gets darker because photosynthesis can't happen in the dark. When the stomata are closed, <u>water can't escape</u>.

2) <u>AN INCREASE IN TEMPERATURE</u> — the <u>warmer</u> it is, the <u>faster</u> transpiration happens. That's because when it's warm the water particles have <u>more energy</u> to evaporate and diffuse out of the stomata. An increase in temperature also <u>increases</u> the <u>rate of photosynthesis</u> and therefore the <u>demand for water</u> — so more is drawn up from the roots.

3) <u>AN INCREASE IN AIR MOVEMENT</u> — if there's <u>lots</u> of air movement (wind) around a leaf, transpiration happens <u>faster</u>. If the air around a leaf is very still, the water vapour just <u>surrounds the leaf</u> and doesn't move away. This means there's a <u>high concentration</u> of water particles outside the leaf as well as inside it, so <u>diffusion</u> doesn't happen as quickly. If it's windy, the water vapour is <u>swept away</u>, maintaining a <u>low concentration</u> of water in the air outside the leaf. Diffusion then happens quickly, from an area of higher concentration to an area of lower concentration.

You Can Measure Loss of Mass to Estimate Transpiration Rate

| PRACTICAL |

You can do an <u>experiment</u> to show this:

1) Add some <u>damp soil</u> to a <u>plastic sandwich bag</u>. Take a <u>small plant</u> and plant it in the soil, then <u>tie the bag shut</u> around the stem (leaving the leaves <u>out</u> of the bag).

2) <u>Measure</u> the <u>mass</u> of the wrapped up plant and <u>record</u> it.

3) <u>Leave</u> the plant in a well-lit place for <u>24 hours</u>, then <u>measure its mass again</u>.

4) You should notice that the plant has <u>decreased in mass</u>. It's assumed this is equal to the mass of the <u>water lost</u> through <u>transpiration</u>.

5) <u>Dividing</u> the <u>mass lost</u> (in grams) by the <u>time taken</u> to lose it (in days) will give you an <u>estimate</u> of the <u>transpiration rate</u> (in g/day).

6) You can <u>compare</u> how much water a plant loses under <u>different conditions</u>, e.g. in the <u>light</u> versus in the <u>dark</u>. To compare them fairly, you need to <u>calculate</u> the <u>percentage change in mass</u>.

> The plant could actually lose a small amount of mass in other ways, e.g. it loses oxygen during photosynthesis.

**EXAMPLE:** A plant weighed 250 g at the start of the experiment. After being exposed to light for 24 hours it weighed 225 g. Calculate the percentage change in mass.

To find the <u>percentage change in mass</u>, use the following <u>formula</u>:

$$\text{percentage change} = \frac{\text{final mass} - \text{initial mass}}{\text{initial mass}} \times 100$$

$$\text{percentage change} = \frac{225 - 250}{250} \times 100 = -10\%$$

It's a negative result because the plant lost mass. If the result was positive the plant would have gained mass.

You can also <u>estimate transpiration</u> rate by <u>measuring water uptake</u> by a plant. There's more on this on the next page.

> If you're asked to calculate the percentage <u>loss</u> in mass, then you don't need to include the minus sign in your answer (because you've already been told that mass was lost).

Transpiration — the plant version of perspiration...

A really handy way to remember the three factors that affect the rate of transpiration is to think about drying your washing. A good day for drying your clothes is when it's sunny, warm and windy. It's the same — fancy that.

Q1 A plant was left in a warm room for 24 hours. It had an initial mass of 262 g and an final mass of 217 g. Calculate the percentage change in mass over the 24 hour period. [2 marks]

Chapter B3 — Living Together — Food and Ecosystems

Using a Potometer

It's time for another experiment — you get to use a piece of equipment you've probably never heard of...

A Potometer can be Used to Measure Water Uptake

A <u>potometer</u> is a special piece of apparatus used to <u>measure water uptake</u> by a plant. This gives an <u>estimate</u> of <u>transpiration rate</u> because <u>water uptake</u> by the plant is <u>related</u> to <u>water loss</u> from the leaves (transpiration). It's <u>not</u> a completely <u>accurate</u> estimate though, because the water <u>taken up</u> by a plant is <u>not all lost</u> through transpiration (e.g. some is used up in <u>photosynthesis</u> and some may be lost from parts of the potometer that aren't <u>sealed</u>). Here's how to use a potometer:

1) <u>Cut</u> a shoot <u>underwater</u> to prevent air from entering the xylem. Cut it at a <u>slant</u> to increase the surface area available for water uptake.

2) <u>Assemble</u> the potometer <u>in water</u> and insert the shoot <u>under water</u>, so no <u>air</u> can enter.

3) Remove the apparatus from the water but keep the end of the capillary tube <u>submerged</u> in a beaker of water.

4) Check that the apparatus is <u>watertight</u> and <u>airtight</u>.

5) <u>Dry</u> the leaves, allow time for the shoot to <u>acclimatise</u> and then <u>shut</u> the tap.

6) Remove the end of the capillary tube from the beaker of water until <u>one air bubble</u> has formed, then put the end of the tube <u>back into the water</u>.

7) Record the <u>starting position</u> of the air bubble.

8) Start a <u>stopwatch</u> and record the <u>distance moved</u> by the bubble per unit time, e.g. per hour. Calculating the <u>speed</u> of <u>air bubble movement</u> allows you to <u>measure water uptake</u>.

9) Keep the <u>conditions constant</u> throughout the experiment, e.g. the <u>temperature</u> and <u>air humidity</u>.

Setting up a potometer is tough — if there are air bubbles in the apparatus or the plant's xylem it will affect your results.

reservoir of water

Tap is shut off during experiment.

Potometers can be set up in different ways. You might see one in the exam that's a bit different to this one but they're all used to estimate transpiration rate.

As the plant takes up water, the air bubble moves along the scale.

Water moves this way.

Bubble moves this way.

capillary tube with a scale

Beaker of water.

 **EXAMPLE:**

A potometer was used to measure the rate of water uptake of a plant cutting. The bubble moved 25 mm in 10 minutes. Calculate the rate of water uptake.

Divide the <u>distance</u> the bubble moved by the <u>time taken</u>.

$$\frac{\text{distance moved}}{\text{time taken}} = \frac{25}{10} = 2.5 \text{ mm / minute}$$

You Can See How Environmental Conditions Affect Water Uptake

You can use a potometer to <u>estimate</u> how different factors affect the <u>rate of water uptake</u>. The set up above will be your <u>control</u> — you can <u>vary</u> an <u>environmental condition</u> (see below), run the experiment again and <u>compare</u> the results to the <u>control</u> to see how the change <u>affected</u> the rate of water uptake.

1) <u>Light intensity</u> — You could use a <u>lamp</u> to <u>increase</u> the <u>intensity of light</u> that hits the plant — this should <u>increase</u> the transpiration rate, and therefore the rate of water uptake. To <u>decrease</u> the light intensity, put the potometer in a <u>cupboard</u> (this should <u>decrease</u> the rate of water uptake).

2) <u>Temperature</u> — You could increase or decrease the temperature by putting the potometer in a <u>room</u> that's <u>warmer</u> or <u>colder</u> than where you did the control experiment. An <u>increase</u> in temperature should <u>increase</u> the rate of water uptake and a <u>decrease</u> in temperature should <u>lower</u> it.

3) <u>Air movement</u> — You could use a <u>fan</u> to <u>increase</u> the air movement around the plant — this should <u>increase</u> the transpiration rate, and therefore the rate of water uptake.

Potometer — a surprisingly useless tool for measuring crockery...

The tricky bit of using a potometer is setting it up — keeping air out and water in is harder than it sounds.

Q1 Give two variables you should keep constant if investigating the effect of temperature on the rate of water uptake.

[2 marks]

Ecosystems and Interactions Between Organisms

It's tough in the wild — there's always competition for food and other resources. So if the environment changes, e.g. there's not enough food or it's too hot, it can be the last straw for some organisms...

Ecosystems are Organised into Different Levels

A habitat is the place where an organism lives, e.g. a rocky shore or a field.

Ecosystems have different levels of organisation:

1) Individual — A single organism.
2) Population — All the organisms of one species in a habitat.
3) Community — All the organisms (different species) living in a habitat.
4) Ecosystem — A community of organisms along with all the non-living (abiotic) conditions (see below).

A species is a group of similar organisms that can reproduce with each other to give fertile offspring.

Organisms Compete for Resources to Survive

Organisms need things from their environment and from other organisms in order to survive and reproduce:

1) Plants need light, space, water and minerals from the soil, as well as seed dispersers (e.g. animals that eat fruit and spread the seeds in their droppings) and pollinators (e.g. bees).

2) Animals need space (territory), shelter, food, water and mates.

The size of a population is limited by competition for these factors as well as predation (see below). Organisms compete with other species (and members of their own species) for the same resources. E.g. red and grey squirrels live in the same habitat and eat the same food. Competition with the grey squirrels for these resources in some areas means there's not enough food for the reds — so the population of red squirrels is decreasing, partly as a result of this.

Environmental Changes Affect Communities in Different Ways

The environment in which plants and animals live changes all the time. These changes are caused by abiotic (non-living) and biotic (living) factors and affect communities in different ways — for some species population size may increase, for others it may decrease, or the distribution of populations (where they live) may change. Here are some examples of the effects of changes in abiotic and biotic factors:

Abiotic Factors Affect Communities...

1) Environmental conditions — e.g. the distribution of bird species in Germany appears to be changing because of a rise in average temperature. Other environmental conditions that affect the abundance and distribution of organisms include light intensity (plants only), moisture level and soil pH.

2) Toxic chemicals — e.g. chemical pesticides or fertilisers. Pesticides can build up in food chains through bioaccumulation — this is where, at each stage of the food chain, concentration of the pesticide increases, so organisms at the top of the chain receive a toxic dose. Excess fertilisers released into lakes and ponds cause increased growth of algae. This is called eutrophication. The algae block sunlight from plants, which die. Microorganisms feeding on the dead plants use up O_2 in the water, leading to the death of other organisms (e.g. fish).

... and so do Biotic Factors

1) Availability of food — e.g. in a bumper year for berries, the population of blackbirds might increase because there'll be enough food for all of them, so they're more likely to survive and reproduce.

2) Number of predators — e.g. if the number of lions (predator) decreases then the number of gazelles (prey) might increase because fewer of them will be eaten by the lions.

3) Presence of pathogens — e.g. if a new pathogen was introduced into the community then populations may decrease due to illness.

The presence of competitors is also a biotic factor that affects the population size and distribution of species.

Revision — an abiotic factor causing stress in my community...

Organisms like everything to be just right — temperature, light, food... I'd never get away with being that fussy.

Q1   Give two abiotic factors that could affect the community in an ecosystem.   [2 marks]

Investigating Ecosystems *PRACTICAL*

Here's how to study the distribution and abundance of organisms. First up, using quadrats...

Use a Quadrat to Study The Distribution of Small Organisms

A quadrat is a square frame enclosing a known area, e.g. 1 m². To compare how common an organism is in two sample areas, just follow these simple steps:

1) Place a 1 m² quadrat on the ground at a random point within the first sample area. E.g. divide the area into a grid and use a random number generator to pick coordinates. Otherwise, if all your samples are in one spot and everywhere else is different, the results you get won't be representative of the whole sample area. For more about random sampling take a look at page 111.

A quadrat

2) Count all the organisms you're interested in within the quadrat.
3) Repeat steps 1 and 2 lots of times. (The larger the sample size the better, see p.101.)
4) Work out the mean number of organisms per quadrat within the first sample area.
5) Repeat steps 1 to 4 in the second sample area.
6) Finally compare the two means. E.g. you might find 2 daisies per m² in the shade, and 22 daisies per m² (lots more) in an open field.

$$\text{Mean} = \frac{\text{total number of organisms}}{\text{number of quadrats}}$$

Estimate Population Sizes by Scaling Up from a Small Sample Area

To work out the population size of an organism in one sample area, you need to work out the mean number of organisms per m² (if your quadrat has an area of 1 m², this is the same as the mean number of organisms per quadrat, worked out above). Then just multiply the mean by the total area of the habitat:

EXAMPLE: Students used 0.25 m² quadrats to randomly sample daisies in a field. They found a mean of 10 daisies per quadrat. The field's area was 800 m². Estimate the population of daisies in the field.

1) Work out the mean number of organisms per m². 1 ÷ 0.25 = 4   4 × 10 = 40 daisies per m²
2) Multiply the mean per m² by the total area (in m²) of the habitat. **40 × 800 = 32 000 daisies in the field**

Use Capture-Mark-Release-Recapture to Estimate Population Sizes

1) Capture a sample of the population and mark the animals in a harmless way.
2) Release them back into the environment (and give the animals time to redistribute into the population).
3) Recapture another sample of the population. Count how many of this sample are marked.
4) Then estimate population size with this equation:

$$\text{Population Size} = \frac{\text{number in first sample} \times \text{number in second sample}}{\text{number in second sample previously marked}}$$

EXAMPLE: 30 woodlice were caught in a pitfall trap in an hour and marked before being released back into the environment. The next day, 35 woodlice were caught in an hour, only 5 of which were marked. Estimate the population size.

All you need to do is put the numbers into the population size equation (shown above).

Population size = (30 × 35) ÷ 5 = **210 woodlice**

number in the first sample   number in the second sample   number in the second sample previously marked

A pitfall trap is a steep-sided container, with an open top, which is sunk into the ground. It's used to trap ground-dwelling insects.

When using the capture-mark-release-recapture method, you have to make a number of assumptions. These include: there has been no change in the population size between the samples (e.g. births and deaths) and the marking hasn't affected individuals' chance of survival (e.g. making them more visible to predators).

Drat, drat and double drat — my favourite use of quadrats...

Choosing which sampling method to use often depends on the type of organism. E.g. quadrats are great for organisms that don't move such as plants, but nets and traps are better for organisms that move around, like insects.

Q1   Capture-mark-release-recapture was used to estimate a population of crabs. In the first sample 22 were caught. A second sample had 26 crabs, 4 of which were marked. Estimate the population size.   [2 marks]

More on Investigating Ecosystems

Yep, there's still some more to learn about this stuff. Coming up we have <u>keys</u> and <u>transects</u> — lovely.

Keys are Used to Identify Creatures

1) A <u>key</u> is a <u>series of questions</u> that you can use to figure out what an <u>unknown organism</u> is.

2) Keys are useful when carrying out sampling as they help you to <u>correctly identify</u> organisms you find.

3) To use a key you start at question 1, and the answer to that question (which you know by looking at your mystery organism) is used to <u>narrow down</u> your options of what it could be.

4) Sometimes keys will just have <u>statements</u>, rather than questions, that are followed by a number of options — e.g. 'number of legs' followed by some different options (see below).

5) As you answer more and more questions you <u>narrow down your options further</u> until eventually you're just <u>left with one</u> possible species your organism could be.

<u>Part of a key</u> is shown on the right. It can be used to identify <u>types of organisms</u> that might be found <u>on the ground</u> in a <u>woodland</u>.

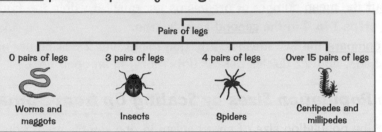

Transects are Used to Investigate Distribution

1) You can investigate how the <u>distribution</u> of an organism <u>gradually changes</u> across an area (e.g. from a hedge towards the middle of a field) using <u>lines</u> called <u>transects</u>.

2) When you sample along the length of a transect using a <u>quadrat</u> (see previous page) this is called a <u>belt transect</u>.

3) To do a <u>belt transect</u> follow the steps below:

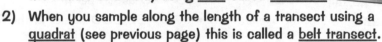

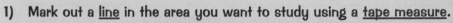

1) Mark out a <u>line</u> in the area you want to study using a <u>tape measure</u>.

2) Place a <u>quadrat</u> at the <u>start</u> of the <u>line</u> and <u>count</u> and <u>record</u> the organisms you find in the quadrat.

3) Then, instead of picking a second sampling site at random (which you'd do if you were sampling a whole area with a quadrat), you take samples by <u>moving</u> your quadrat <u>along the line</u>, e.g. placing the quadrat at <u>intervals</u> of every <u>2 m</u>.

4) You could even take samples along the <u>entire length</u> of your transect by placing your quadrats right <u>next to each other</u>. This might take <u>ages</u> if you have a long transect though.

5) <u>Repeat</u> your transect at least <u>twice</u> more at different places within the area you want to study.

4) If it's difficult to count all the individual organisms in the quadrat (e.g. if they're grass) you can calculate the <u>percentage cover</u>. This means estimating the percentage <u>area</u> of the quadrat covered by a particular type of organism, e.g. by <u>counting</u> the number of little squares covered by the organisms.

5) Taking <u>measurements</u> of <u>abiotic factors</u> (see next page) at points along the transect can show how changes in these affect the distribution and abundance of organisms in the habitat. E.g. in a coastal habitat, changes in <u>salinity</u> and <u>soil depth</u> result in zones where different plants grow.

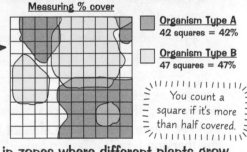

Measuring % cover

Organism Type A
42 squares = 42%

Organism Type B
47 squares = 47%

You count a square if it's more than half covered.

Identification keys — not much use in the world of home security...

Keys help you identify organisms you've found when sampling. This is pretty important when you want to talk about the different organisms that you've seen — it's not much use saying you found six slimy things in a pond...

Q1 Describe how to carry out a belt transect. [3 marks]

Investigating Factors Affecting Distribution

The way organisms are distributed depends on a number of different factors. Prepare to learn all about them.

The Distribution of Organisms is Affected by Abiotic and Biotic Factors

1) The distribution of organisms is affected by abiotic factors such as temperature, moisture level, light intensity and soil pH (see page 44). For example, in a playing field, you might find that daisies are more common in the open than under trees, because there's more light available in the open.

2) Biotic factors can also affect the distribution of organisms (see p.44). E.g. competition between species might result in a different distribution of these species than if this competition didn't exist.

You Need to Know How to Measure Abiotic Factors   PRACTICAL

If you find there's a difference in the distribution of organisms, you can investigate the factors that might be causing it. For example, when looking into the distribution of daisies in the playing field mentioned above, you could measure light intensity both under the trees and in the open — finding a difference in light intensity could provide evidence for the idea that this is affecting the distribution of daisies.

Here's how you can measure the following abiotic factors:

There's more on measuring temperature and pH on p.113.

1) Use a thermometer to measure the temperature in different places.

2) Use a soil moisture meter to measure the level of moisture in some soil.

3) Use an electronic device called a light meter to measure light intensity. Hold the meter at the level of the organisms you're investigating (ground level for daisies) and make sure it's at the same height and angle for every reading you take.

4) Measure soil pH using indicator liquid — water is added to a soil sample and then an indicator liquid (e.g. Universal indicator) is added that changes colour depending on the pH. The colour is compared to a chart to find out the pH of the soil. Electronic pH monitors can be used to produce a more accurate pH value for the sample being tested.

The Distribution of Indicator Species Can Be Used to Assess Pollution

Some organisms are very sensitive to changes in their environment and can be studied to see how polluted an area is — these organisms are known as indicator species.

PRACTICAL

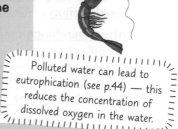

- Some invertebrate animals, like stonefly larvae and freshwater shrimps are good indicators for water pollution because they're very sensitive to the concentration of dissolved oxygen in the water — If you find stonefly larvae in a river, it indicates that the water is clean.

- Other invertebrate species have adapted to live in polluted conditions — so if you see a lot of them you know there's a problem. E.g. blood worms and sludge worms indicate highly polluted water.

Polluted water can lead to eutrophication (see p.44) — this reduces the concentration of dissolved oxygen in the water.

- Air pollution can be monitored by looking at particular types of lichen that are very sensitive to the concentration of sulfur dioxide in the atmosphere. (Sulfur dioxide is a pollutant released from car exhausts, power stations, etc.) E.g. the air is clean if there are lots of lichen — especially bushy lichen, which need cleaner air than crusty lichen.

When investigating indicator species, you need to sample them. Sampling methods will vary depending on the species you're interested in and where it is found. For example, aquatic organisms could be caught with a net which is swept through the water. Lichens (which grow on trees and rocks and don't move about) could be sampled using quadrats or transects (see pages 45-46).

Teenagers are an indicator species — not found in clean rooms...

Don't forget that the absence of an indicator species could mean the opposite of what they indicate. E.g. the absence of stonefly larvae could indicate polluted water. Nice and simple, innit?

Q1   Bushy lichen grows on trees in the local park. Explain what this indicates about the air quality.   [2 marks]

Food Chains and Food Webs

If you like <u>food</u>, and you like <u>chains</u>, then <u>food chains</u> might just blow your mind. Strap yourself in and prepare for some 'edge of your seat' learning, because the show is about to begin...

Food Chains Show What's Eaten by What in an Ecosystem

1) <u>Food chains</u> always start with a <u>producer</u>.
   Producers <u>make</u> (produce) <u>their own food</u> using energy from the Sun.

2) Producers are usually <u>green plants</u> — they make <u>glucose</u> by <u>photosynthesis</u> (see p.34).

3) When a green plant produces glucose, some of it is used to make <u>other biological molecules</u> in the plant. These biological molecules are the plant's <u>biomass</u> — the <u>mass</u> of <u>living material</u>. Biomass can be thought of as <u>energy stored</u> in a plant.

4) <u>Biomass</u> is <u>transferred</u> through living organisms in an ecosystem when organisms <u>eat</u> other organisms — this means that these photosynthetic organisms <u>support nearly all life on Earth</u>.

5) Producers are eaten by <u>primary consumers</u> (herbivores). Primary consumers are then eaten by <u>secondary consumers</u> (carnivores) and secondary consumers are eaten by <u>tertiary consumers</u> (also carnivores). Here's an example of a food chain:

Producers   Primary consumers   Secondary consumer

<u>5000</u> dandelions... feed...   <u>100</u> rabbits... which feed...   <u>1</u> fox.

> Consumers are organisms that eat other organisms. Herbivores are animals that eat plants, and carnivores are animals that eat other animals.

6) Each stage in a food chain is called a <u>trophic level</u>. <u>Producers</u> are the <u>first</u> trophic level.

Food Webs Show How Food Chains are Linked

1) There are many different species within an environment — which means <u>lots of different</u> possible <u>food chains</u>. You can draw a <u>food web</u> to show them.

2) All the species in a food web are <u>interdependent</u> — they <u>depend</u> on each other for survival.

3) The <u>transfer of biomass</u> is one way in which organisms are <u>interdependent</u>. The <u>direction</u> of biomass transfer is shown by the <u>arrows</u> in a food chain or web.

4) <u>Interdependence</u> means that a change in the size of one population will affect the sizes of other populations in the community.

> Food webs don't show how much biomass is at each trophic level — it can be shown using pyramids of biomass (see next page).

<u>For example</u>, in the food web on the right, if lots of <u>water spiders died</u>, then:

- There would be <u>less food</u> for the <u>frogs</u>, so their numbers might <u>decrease</u>.
- The number of <u>mayfly larvae</u> might <u>increase</u> since the water spiders wouldn't be eating them.
- The <u>diving beetles</u> wouldn't be <u>competing</u> with the water spiders for food, so their numbers might <u>increase</u>.

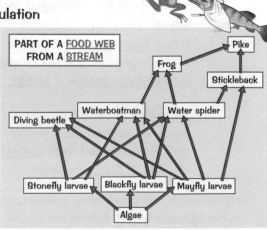

PART OF A <u>FOOD WEB</u> FROM A <u>STREAM</u>

Pike · Frog · Stickleback · Waterboatman · Water spider · Diving beetle · Stonefly larvae · Blackfly larvae · Mayfly larvae · Algae

---

Food webs — nothing to do with ordering pizza online, I'm afraid...

Food webs are handy for looking at relationships between individual species. Unfortunately you hardly ever see simple food webs in the real world — they're normally as tangled together and interlinked as a bowl of spaghetti.

Q1   The diagram on the right shows part of a food web.
     Using the diagram, suggest what might happen to the
     other species if the population of mice increased.

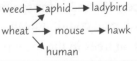

weed → aphid → ladybird
wheat → mouse → hawk
       ↘ human

[4 marks]

Pyramids of Biomass and Number

The amount of <u>biomass</u> (the mass of living material) <u>decreases</u> as you move up a trophic level. <u>Pyramids of biomass</u> are used as <u>models</u> to show how the biomass <u>changes</u>.

You Need to be able to Understand and Draw Pyramids of Biomass

Luckily it's pretty easy — they'll give you all the information you need to do it in the exam. Here's an example of a <u>food chain</u> you might be given:

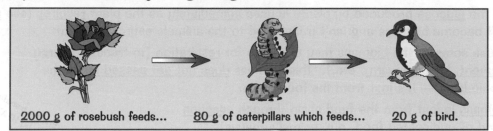

<u>2000 g</u> of rosebush feeds...   <u>80 g</u> of caterpillars which feeds...   <u>20 g</u> of bird.

1) Each bar on a <u>pyramid of biomass</u> shows the <u>mass of living material</u> at that stage of the food chain — basically how much all the organisms at each level would '<u>weigh</u>' if you put them <u>all together</u>.

2) So the '<u>rosebush</u>' bar on this pyramid would need to be <u>longer</u> than the '<u>caterpillars</u>' bar, which in turn should be <u>longer</u> than the '<u>bird</u>' bar... and so on.

3) The <u>rosebush</u> goes at the <u>bottom</u> because it's at the bottom of the food chain — it's the producer.

4) Then the <u>primary consumers</u> (caterpillars) go on top of the <u>producer</u>, the <u>secondary consumers</u> (birds) go on top of the <u>primary consumers</u>, and so on.

20 g	bird
80 g	caterpillars
2000 g	rosebush

5) Biomass pyramids are almost <u>always pyramid-shaped</u> because <u>biomass is lost</u> at each stage in the food chain (see next page).

6) It can sometimes be <u>difficult</u> to construct an <u>accurate</u> pyramid of biomass because some organisms feed at <u>more than one</u> trophic level. For example, in the food chain shown on the next page, <u>birds</u> might feed on both <u>ladybirds and greenflies</u>.

Pyramids of Numbers can be Different Shapes

1) <u>Pyramids of numbers</u> are similar to <u>pyramids of biomass</u>, but each bar on a <u>pyramid of numbers</u> shows the <u>number of organisms</u> at that stage of the food chain — <u>not</u> their <u>mass</u>.

2) <u>Pyramids of numbers</u> are sometimes <u>other shapes</u> (not just pyramids):

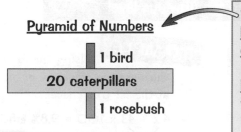

<u>Pyramid of Numbers</u>

1 bird
20 caterpillars
1 rosebush

The '<u>caterpillars</u>' bar on this pyramid is <u>longer</u> than the '<u>rosebush</u>' bar, because <u>one</u> rosebush can feed a <u>number</u> of caterpillars. (But the <u>biomass</u> of the rosebush is much <u>bigger</u> than the biomass of the caterpillars — which is why the biomass pyramid (see above) is the right shape.)

Constructing pyramids is a breeze — just ask the Egyptians...

Pyramids of numbers could also have a big bar across the top if, for example, there were loads of fleas feeding on one fox. But the tiny fleas would still have less biomass than the fox, so the biomass pyramid would look normal.

Q1   Look at the two diagrams on the right. One is a pyramid of biomass and one is a pyramid of numbers. Which one is the pyramid of numbers? Explain your answer.

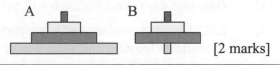

[2 marks]

Chapter B3 — Living Together — Food and Ecosystems

Biomass Transfer

Great, steak for dinner — some <u>biomass</u> from a cow to help you <u>grow</u>. But you'll need some of that biomass for <u>respiration</u>, so you can <u>move about</u> and <u>revise</u>. And some will be <u>indigestible</u>. This is how biomass is <u>lost</u>...

Biomass is Lost Between each Trophic Level

1) <u>Energy</u> (stored as <u>biomass</u>) is <u>transferred</u> through the living organisms of an ecosystem when organisms <u>eat</u> other organisms. However, <u>not much biomass</u> gets transferred from one <u>trophic level</u> to the <u>next</u>.

2) Some of the <u>glucose</u> produced by plants is used <u>immediately</u> as the plant <u>respires</u> (see p.57). It doesn't become biomass and isn't transferred to the animals eating the plant.

3) <u>Animals</u> use some of the <u>biomass</u> they consume for <u>respiration</u> (to transfer energy for <u>movement</u>, <u>keeping warm</u>, etc.). This biomass <u>does not get passed on</u> to the next trophic level — it's <u>lost</u> from the food chain.

4) <u>More biomass</u> is lost from the food chain through <u>egestion</u> (getting rid of <u>undigested food</u>, e.g. animal's <u>faeces</u>).

5) Biomass is also lost from a food chain because <u>not all</u> of every organism gets <u>eaten</u> (e.g. bones and plant roots aren't usually eaten).

6) This all explains why you get <u>biomass pyramids</u> — most biomass is lost, so <u>doesn't</u> get to the <u>next level up</u>.

7) It also explains why you hardly ever get <u>food chains</u> with more than about <u>five trophic levels</u>. So much <u>biomass</u> is <u>lost</u> at each stage that there's <u>not enough left</u> to support organisms after that many stages. You also tend to get <u>fewer organisms</u> at each <u>trophic level</u> (although this isn't always the case — see pyramids of number on previous page).

Energy transferred by HEAT — MOVEMENT

EGESTION

You Need to be Able to Interpret Data on Biomass Transfer

1) The numbers show the <u>amount of biomass</u> available to the <u>next level</u>. So <u>43 kg</u> is the amount of biomass available to the <u>greenflies</u>, and <u>4.2 kg</u> is the amount available to the <u>ladybirds</u>.

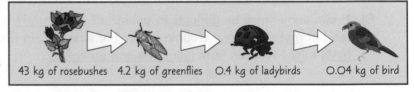

43 kg of rosebushes   4.2 kg of greenflies   0.4 kg of ladybirds   0.04 kg of bird

2) You can work out how much biomass has been <u>lost</u> at each level by taking away the biomass that is available to the <u>next</u> level from the biomass that was available from the <u>previous</u> level.

3) You can also calculate the <u>efficiency of biomass transfer</u> — this just means how good it is at passing on biomass from one level to the next.

$$\text{efficiency} = \frac{\text{biomass available to the next level}}{\text{biomass that was available to the previous level}} \times 100$$

The 'efficiency of biomass transfer' is sometimes referred to as the 'percentage biomass transferred'.

EXAMPLE: Using the food chain above, calculate the biomass lost at the 1st trophic level through respiration and waste products.

43 − 4.2 = 39 kg (to 2 s.f.)

Biomass at 1st trophic level.   Biomass at 2nd trophic level.

EXAMPLE: Using the food chain above, calculate the efficiency of biomass transfer at the 1st tropic level.

4.2 ÷ 43 × 100 = 9.8% efficient (to 2 s.f.)

Put the values into the equation shown above.

Spaghetti necklaces are my favourite type of food chain...

Staying alive is important, but it sure does require a lot of biomass. Organisms really aren't very efficient at transferring biomass to the next trophic level — they lose loads through respiration and so on. Chew on that...

Q1   Give two ways that biomass is lost between trophic levels.   [2 marks]

Q2   Calculate the percentage efficiency of biomass transfer between some large fish with 995 kg of available biomass and a shark with 110 kg of available biomass.   [1 mark]

Making and Breaking Biological Molecules

Organisms can break big molecules down into smaller ones and build small molecules back up into bigger ones. It's pretty clever stuff, and all given a helping hand by our good friends, enzymes (see p.32).

Carbohydrates, Lipids and Proteins are Organic Molecules

Organic molecules are molecules that contain carbon. Carbohydrates, lipids and proteins are all organic molecules and so are the smaller molecules they're made up from:

1) **Long-chain carbohydrates**, e.g. starch are made from simple sugars.

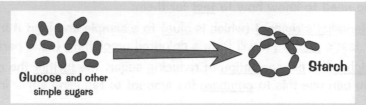

2) **Proteins** are made from amino acids.

3) **Lipids** are made by joining fatty acids and glycerol.

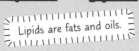
Lipids are fats and oils.

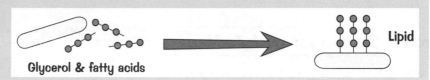

Plants Build Up Organic Molecules in their Biomass

1) Producers take in the elements they need to survive from their environment, e.g. plants take in carbon from the air and nitrogen compounds from the soil.

2) Producers use carbon (along with oxygen and hydrogen) to make glucose during photosynthesis (see page 34).

3) Glucose is then used to make other small organic molecules, e.g. other sugars, fatty acids and glycerol. Glucose and nitrate ions (see page 38) are combined to make amino acids.

4) These small molecules are then used by the producer to create long-chain carbohydrates, lipids and proteins. For example, amino acids are joined together to make proteins.

5) These larger molecules are used to build structures like cell membranes and organelles.

6) All these synthesis reactions are catalysed by enzymes.

Animals Break these Molecules Down, then Build them Up Again

1) Unlike plants, consumers can only get carbon and nitrogen compounds by eating and digesting the large organic molecules in producers or other consumers in the food chain.

2) Digestion breaks these large molecules down into smaller ones, which can be more easily absorbed by the consumer. Proteins are broken down into amino acids, starch is broken down into simple sugars, and lipids are broken down into fatty acids and glycerol. Digestion reactions are also catalysed by enzymes.

3) The small molecules are then transported to the consumer's cells (usually in the blood supply) to be built up into larger molecules (proteins, etc.) again. These form the biomass of the consumer.

What do you call an acid that's eaten all the pies...

Make sure you learn the diagrams at the top of the page really well (I mean, really, really well). And remember that when the bigger organic molecules get broken down, the arrow just goes the opposite way.

Q1   Name the molecules that result from the breakdown of: a) carbohydrates, b) proteins.   [2 marks]

Chapter B3 — Living Together — Food and Ecosystems

PRACTICAL | Testing for Biological Molecules

You need to know how you can <u>test</u> for <u>biological molecules</u> using <u>different chemicals</u>. The tests are all <u>qualitative</u> — you can tell <u>whether or not</u> a substance is <u>present</u> in a sample, but <u>not how much</u> is present.

You Can Test for Sugars Using Benedict's Reagent

There are lots of different types of <u>sugar molecules</u>. Due to their <u>chemical properties</u>, many sugars (e.g. glucose) are called <u>reducing sugars</u>. You don't need to know exactly what reducing sugars are, but you do need to know how to <u>test</u> for them:

1) Add <u>Benedict's reagent</u> (which is <u>blue</u>) to a sample and <u>heat</u> it in a water bath that's set to <u>75 °C</u>. If the test's <u>positive</u> it will form a <u>coloured precipitate</u> (solid particles suspended in the solution).

2) The <u>higher</u> the <u>concentration</u> of reducing sugar, the <u>further</u> the colour change goes — you can use this to <u>compare</u> the amount of reducing sugar in different solutions.

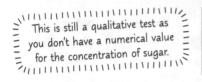
This is still a qualitative test as you don't have a numerical value for the concentration of sugar.

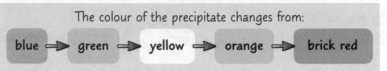
The colour of the precipitate changes from:
blue ⟹ green ⟹ yellow ⟹ orange ⟹ brick red

Starch is Tested for with Iodine

Iodine solution is iodine dissolved in potassium iodide solution.

Just add <u>iodine solution</u> to the test sample.

1) If starch <u>is present</u>, the sample changes from <u>browny-orange</u> to a dark, <u>blue-black</u> colour.

2) If there's <u>no starch</u>, it stays browny-orange.

Use the Emulsion Test for Lipids

An emulsion is when one liquid doesn't dissolve in another — it just forms little droplets.

To find out if there are any <u>lipids</u> in a sample:

1) <u>Shake</u> the test substance with <u>ethanol</u> for about a minute until it <u>dissolves</u>, then pour the solution into <u>water</u>.

2) If there <u>are</u> any <u>lipids present</u>, they will show up as a <u>milky emulsion</u>.

3) The <u>more lipid</u> there is, the <u>more noticeable</u> the milky colour will be.

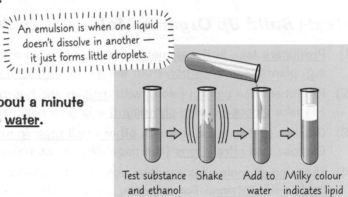
Test substance and ethanol | Shake | Add to water | Milky colour indicates lipid

The Biuret Test is Used for Proteins

If you needed to find out if a sample contains <u>protein</u> you'd use the <u>biuret test</u>:

1) First, add a few drops of <u>sodium hydroxide</u> solution to make the solution <u>alkaline</u>.

2) Then add some <u>copper(II) sulfate</u> solution (which is <u>bright blue</u>).

- If there's <u>no protein</u>, the solution will stay <u>blue</u>.
- If protein <u>is present</u>, the solution will turn <u>purple</u>.

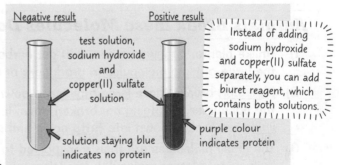
Negative result — test solution, sodium hydroxide and copper(II) sulfate solution — solution staying blue indicates no protein
Positive result — purple colour indicates protein
Instead of adding sodium hydroxide and copper(II) sulfate separately, you can add biuret reagent, which contains both solutions.

The Anger Test — annoy test subject. Red face = anger present...

OK, so this stuff isn't thrilling but learning it is better than being dissolved in a giant vat of vinegar. Yowch.

Q1 A solution that has been mixed with sodium hydroxide and copper(II) sulfate solution turns purple. What conclusion would you draw from this test? [1 mark]

Cycles in Ecosystems

Substances like <u>carbon</u> and <u>water</u> are <u>essential</u> to <u>life</u> on Earth. Luckily for us, they flow through the Earth's <u>ecosystems</u> in <u>cycles</u>, meaning that we (and other organisms) can <u>reuse them</u> over and over again — splendid.

Materials are Constantly Recycled in an Ecosystem

1) Remember, an <u>ecosystem</u> is a <u>community</u> of <u>organisms</u> living in an area, as well as all the <u>non-living</u> (abiotic) conditions, e.g. soil quality, availability of water, temperature. There's more on these on p.44.

2) Materials organisms need to survive, such as <u>carbon</u> and <u>water</u> (see next page) are <u>recycled</u> through <u>both</u> the <u>biotic</u> and <u>abiotic</u> components of ecosystems.

3) This means they pass through both <u>living organisms</u> (the biotic components of an ecosystem) and things like the <u>air</u>, <u>rocks</u> and <u>soil</u> (abiotic components of an ecosystem) in a <u>continuous cycle</u>.

The Carbon Cycle Shows How Carbon is Recycled

<u>Carbon</u> is an important element in the materials that living things are made from. But there's only a <u>fixed amount</u> of carbon in the world. This means it's constantly <u>recycled</u>:

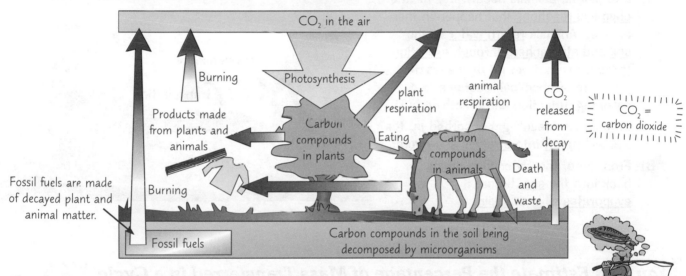

This diagram isn't half as bad as it looks. <u>Learn</u> these important points:

1) There's only <u>one arrow</u> going <u>down</u> from <u>CO_2</u> in the air. The whole thing is 'powered' by <u>photosynthesis</u>. Green <u>plants</u> use the carbon from <u>CO_2</u> to make <u>carbohydrates</u>, <u>lipids</u> and <u>proteins</u>.

2) <u>Eating</u> passes the carbon compounds in the plant along to <u>animals</u> in a food chain or web (see p.48).

3) Both plant and animal <u>respiration</u> while the organisms are alive <u>releases CO_2</u> back into the <u>air</u>.

4) Plants and animals eventually <u>die</u> and <u>decompose</u>, or are killed and turned into <u>useful products</u>.

5) When plants and animals decompose they're broken down by microorganisms, such as <u>bacteria</u> and <u>fungi</u>. These microorganisms are known as <u>decomposers</u> and they release <u>enzymes</u>, which <u>catalyse</u> the breakdown of dead material into <u>smaller molecules</u>. Decomposers <u>release</u> <u>CO_2</u> back into the air by <u>respiration</u> (see page 57) as they break down the material.

6) Some useful plant and animal <u>products</u>, e.g. wood and fossil fuels, are burned (<u>combustion</u>). This also releases <u>CO_2</u> back into the air.

7) <u>Decomposition</u> of materials means that <u>habitats</u> can be <u>maintained</u> for the organisms that live there, e.g. <u>nutrients</u> are <u>returned</u> to the soil and <u>waste material</u>, such as dead leaves, doesn't just <u>pile up</u>.

The Carbon Cycle — a great gift for any bike enthusiast...

Carbon atoms are very important — they're found in plants, animals, your petrol tank and on your burnt toast.

Q1   Suggest two reasons why chopping down trees can increase the concentration of CO_2 in the air.   [2 marks]

More on Cycles in Ecosystems

Like carbon, <u>water</u> on planet Earth is constantly <u>recycled</u>. This is lucky for us because <u>without water</u>, we <u>wouldn't survive</u>. And I don't just mean there'd be no paddling pools, ice lollies or bubble baths...

The Water Cycle Means Water is Endlessly Recycled

1) <u>Energy</u> from the <u>Sun</u> makes water <u>evaporate</u> from the land and sea, turning it into <u>water vapour</u>.

2) Water also evaporates from plants — this is known as <u>transpiration</u> (see p.40).

3) The warm water vapour is <u>carried upwards</u> (as warm air rises). When it gets higher up it <u>cools</u> and <u>condenses</u> to form <u>clouds</u>.

4) Water falls from the clouds as <u>precipitation</u> (usually rain, but sometimes snow or hail) onto <u>land</u>.

5) Some of this water is <u>absorbed</u> by the <u>soil</u> and is taken up by <u>plant roots</u>. This provides plants with <u>fresh water</u> for things like <u>photosynthesis</u>. Some of the water taken up by plants becomes part of the plants' <u>tissues</u> and is passed along to <u>animals</u> in <u>food chains</u>.

6) Like plants, animals need water for the <u>chemical reactions</u> that happen in their bodies. Animals <u>return water</u> to the <u>soil</u> and <u>atmosphere</u> through <u>excretion</u> (processes that get rid of the waste products of chemical reactions, e.g. sweating, urination and breathing out).

7) Water that doesn't get absorbed by the soil will <u>runoff</u> into <u>streams</u> and <u>rivers</u>.

8) From here, the water then <u>drains</u> back into the <u>sea</u>, before it <u>evaporates</u> all over <u>again</u>.

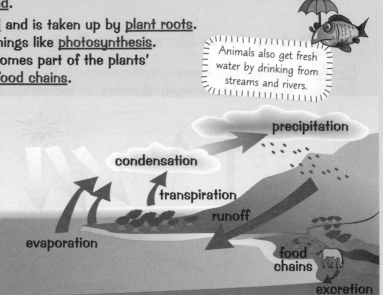

As with carbon, there has only ever been a fixed amount of water on the Earth.

Animals also get fresh water by drinking from streams and rivers.

You Can Estimate the Percentage of Mass Transferred in a Cycle

1) In the <u>exams</u>, you might be asked to calculate <u>percentage masses</u> in the context of cycles.

2) For example, you might be asked to calculate the <u>mass of carbon</u> released in an animal's <u>waste</u> as a <u>percentage</u> of the mass of carbon the animal takes in from its <u>food</u>. Or you might be asked to calculate the <u>mass of water</u> a <u>tree</u> transfers to the environment through <u>transpiration</u> as a percentage of the mass of water it takes in through its <u>roots</u>.

> **EXAMPLE:**
> A tree takes in 4000 kg of water in a day through its roots. It loses 3960 kg of water in a day through transpiration. Calculate the percentage mass of water transferred from the plant roots to the atmosphere through transpiration.
>
> percentage mass of water transferred $= \dfrac{3960}{4000} \times 100 = 99\%$

Come on out, it's only a little water cycle, it won't hurt you...

The most important thing to remember is that it's a cycle — a continuous process with no beginning or end. Water that falls to the ground as rain (or any other kind of precipitation) will eventually end up back in the clouds again.

Q1   a) In the water cycle, how does water move from the land into the air?   [1 mark]

       b) How does the water cycle benefit plants and animals?   [1 mark]

Decomposition

Decomposition is really important — without it there'd be <u>dead stuff</u> and <u>waste material</u> piling up everywhere. So hurrah for the little <u>microorganisms</u> who aren't afraid of a bit of roadkill for breakfast. Yum.

Microorganisms Help Recycle Materials Through Decomposition

As you may remember from page 53, waste products and dead organisms are <u>broken down</u> by <u>decomposers</u>. The main type of decomposers are <u>microorganisms</u>, such as <u>bacteria</u> and <u>fungi</u>.

Learn These Factors that Affect the Rate of Decomposition

The <u>rate of decomposition</u> is affected by the following <u>environmental factors</u>:

1) <u>Oxygen availability</u> — Many decomposers need <u>oxygen</u> for <u>aerobic respiration</u> (see page 57) so the rate of decomposition <u>increases</u> where there is <u>plenty of oxygen</u> available. When there are <u>low oxygen levels</u>, the rate of decomposition is <u>slower</u>. Some decomposers can respire <u>anaerobically</u> (without oxygen — see p.58) but this transfers <u>less energy</u>, so these decomposers work more <u>slowly</u>.

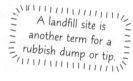
Hooray!

2) <u>Temperature</u> — Most decomposers work best in <u>warm</u> conditions — the rate of decomposition is <u>highest</u> at around 50 °C. This is because decomposers contain <u>enzymes</u>, which <u>digest</u> the dead/waste material. The <u>rate</u> of enzyme-controlled reactions <u>varies</u> with <u>temperature</u> — at <u>lower</u> temperatures the rate of reaction is <u>slower</u> and above certain temperatures the enzymes become <u>denatured</u> and the <u>reaction stops</u>.

See p.32 for more on enzymes.

3) <u>Water content</u> — Decomposers need <u>water</u> to <u>survive</u>, so the rate of decomposition <u>increases</u> in <u>moist conditions</u>. However, <u>waterlogged</u> soils don't contain much <u>oxygen</u> (which many decomposers need to <u>respire</u> — see above) so the rate <u>decreases</u> if there is <u>too much water</u>.

Decomposers in Landfill Sites Contribute to Global Warming

1) <u>Greenhouse gases</u> such as <u>methane</u> and CO_2 naturally <u>trap energy</u> in the <u>atmosphere</u> — this helps to keep the Earth <u>warm</u>. But <u>increasing levels</u> of greenhouse gases are causing the <u>global temperature</u> to <u>rise</u>. This is <u>global warming</u>.

2) <u>Landfill sites</u> tend to be <u>low in O_2</u> — this means there are lots of <u>decomposers</u> respiring <u>anaerobically</u>.

3) Anaerobic respiration by decomposers produces <u>methane</u>, which has a much <u>greater greenhouse effect</u> than the CO_2 produced during aerobic decomposition. So landfill sites contribute <u>more</u> to global warming than natural decomposition in ecosystems.

A landfill site is another term for a rubbish dump or tip.

You can Calculate the Rate of Decomposition

You need to be able to <u>calculate</u> the <u>rate</u> at which biological material <u>decomposes</u>. Here's an <u>example</u>:

EXAMPLE: A block of cheese was left out of the fridge. The graph below shows the amount of mould that formed on the cheese. Mould is a fungus that decomposes the cheese.

Calculate the average rate at which the cheese decomposed during the first week, giving your answer as units of mould/day.

1) Draw a <u>line</u> on your graph at <u>7 days</u> and <u>read off</u> the <u>amount</u> of mould that had formed.

2) <u>Divide</u> the amount of mould by the number of days. $\dfrac{25}{7}$

3) <u>Calculate</u> the answer and don't forget to give the <u>units</u>. = 3.6 units of mould/day

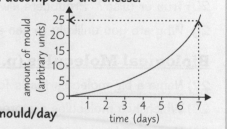

G, G, G, E♭, F, F, F, D — sorry, just decomposing Beethoven's 5th...

Greenhouse gases trap energy that keeps our planet warm — without them we wouldn't survive. It's their increasing levels and Earth's increasing temperatures that worry people. Landfill sites contribute to the increasing methane level.

Q1   Compost is decayed remains of animal and plant matter that can be used as fertiliser.
      Give two things you could do to make sure that compost decomposes quickly.

[2 marks]

Revision Questions for Chapter B3

It's time to say goodbye to Chapter B3 — but not before a healthy dose of questions to test yourself with...
- Try these questions and <u>tick off each one</u> when you <u>get it right</u>.
- When you've done <u>all the questions</u> for a topic and are <u>completely happy</u> with it, tick off the topic.

Enzymes (p.32-33) ☑

1) What part of an enzyme makes it specific to a particular substrate? ☑
2) Explain how temperature affects enzyme activity. ☑
3) State two ways in which you could measure the rate of an enzyme-controlled reaction. ☑

Photosynthesis (p.34-36) ☑

4) Where in a plant cell does photosynthesis take place? ☑
5) What is the equation for photosynthesis? ☑
6) In the inverse square law, how are light intensity and distance linked? ☑
7) What effect would a low carbon dioxide concentration have on the rate of photosynthesis? ☑

Methods of Transport and Transport in Plants (p.37-43) ☑

8) Define the following terms: a) diffusion,   b) osmosis,   c) active transport. ☑
9) Why do multicellular organisms such as plants need specialised exchange surfaces? ☑
10) If a potato cylinder is placed in a solution with a very high sucrose concentration,
    what will happen to the mass of the potato cylinder over time? Explain why. ☑
11) What is translocation? ☑
12) Which type of plant transport vessel is made up of dead cells? ☑
13) How do stomata open and close? ☑
14) Give three factors that affect the rate of transpiration. ☑

Ecosystems and Interactions Between Organisms (p.44-48) ☑

15) Give two resources that plants compete for in ecosystems. ☑
16) Briefly describe how you could use quadrats to investigate the population size of a species. ☑
17) What is an indicator species and why might you sample one? ☑
18) How do food webs show interdependence? ☑

Pyramids of Biomass and Biomass Transfer (p.49-50) ☑

19) What does each bar on a pyramid of biomass represent? ☑
20) True or false? Producers always go at the top of a pyramid of biomass. ☑
21) Why are you unlikely to see a food chain with 10 trophic levels? ☑

Biological Molecules (p.51-52) ☑

22) Name a big molecule that's formed from simple sugars. ☑
23) Which two molecules are produced when lipids are broken down? ☑
24) How would you test for the presence of lipids in a sample? ☑

Cycles in Ecosystems and Decomposition (p.53-55) ☑

25) Name two processes that put carbon back into the air in the carbon cycle. ☑
26) What is the role of microorganisms in the carbon cycle? ☑
27) Give three factors that affect the rate of decomposition. ☑

Respiration

You need <u>energy</u> to keep your body going. Energy comes from <u>food</u>, and it's <u>transferred</u> by <u>respiration</u>.

Respiration is NOT "Breathing In and Out"

1) <u>Respiration</u> is the process of <u>transferring energy</u> from the <u>breakdown of glucose</u> (a sugar).

2) <u>Plants</u> make their own glucose for respiration through <u>photosynthesis</u> (see p.34). <u>Animals</u> (consumers) produce glucose by <u>breaking down</u> the <u>biomass</u> they get when they <u>eat</u> other organisms (see p.51).

3) Organisms need the energy transferred by respiration to <u>survive</u> — so respiration happens <u>continuously</u> in <u>every cell</u> in <u>all living organisms</u>.

4) The energy transferred by respiration <u>can't be used directly</u> by cells — so it's used to make a substance called <u>ATP</u>. ATP <u>stores</u> the energy, which is then used for essential processes, such as <u>breaking</u> and <u>making molecules</u>, <u>active transport</u> (see p.37) and <u>contracting muscles</u> (in animals only).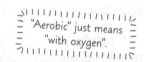

5) Cellular respiration actually involves <u>several different</u> chemical <u>reactions</u>. These are all <u>controlled</u> by <u>enzymes</u>, so the overall <u>rate</u> of respiration is affected by both <u>temperature</u> and <u>pH</u> (see p.32). Cellular respiration is also <u>exothermic</u> — it transfers <u>energy</u> to the <u>environment</u> (by <u>heat</u>).

6) Cells can respire using <u>glucose</u> as a substrate, but organisms can also break down <u>other organic molecules</u> (such as other <u>carbohydrates</u>, <u>proteins</u> and <u>lipids</u>) to use as <u>substrates</u> for respiration.

7) There are <u>two types</u> of respiration, <u>aerobic</u> and <u>anaerobic</u>.

Aerobic Respiration Needs Plenty of Oxygen

1) <u>Aerobic respiration</u> is what happens when there's <u>plenty of oxygen</u> available. It breaks down <u>glucose</u> and combines the products with <u>oxygen</u> to make <u>carbon dioxide</u> (a waste product) and <u>water</u>.

2) Aerobic respiration is the most efficient way to transfer <u>energy</u> from <u>glucose</u>. It produces <u>lots</u> of <u>ATP</u> — <u>32</u> molecules per molecule of glucose.

3) Here is the overall <u>equation</u> for aerobic respiration:

$$\text{glucose} + \text{oxygen} \longrightarrow \text{carbon dioxide} + \text{water}$$
$$C_6H_{12}O_6 + 6O_2 \longrightarrow 6CO_2 + 6H_2O$$

"Aerobic" just means "with oxygen".

4) In <u>eukaryotic</u> (e.g. plant and animal) <u>cells</u>, aerobic respiration mostly takes place in subcellular structures called <u>mitochondria</u> (see p.2). The mitochondria contain most of the <u>enzymes</u> needed to control aerobic respiration reactions.

mitochondria

5) In <u>prokaryotic cells</u> (microorganisms such as bacteria) all aerobic respiration reactions take place in the <u>cytoplasm</u>.

You Can Investigate the Effect of Different Substrates on Respiration Rate

You can investigate how the rate of respiration in <u>yeast</u> is affected by <u>different substrates</u>, e.g. <u>glucose</u> or <u>sucrose</u>. Here's one way to do it:

PRACTICAL

1) Put a <u>set volume</u> and <u>concentration</u> of <u>substrate solution</u> in a <u>test tube</u>.

2) Put the test tube in a <u>water bath</u> set to <u>25 °C</u>.

3) Add a <u>set mass</u> of <u>yeast</u> to the test tube and stir for <u>2 minutes</u>.

4) Attach the test tube to a <u>gas syringe</u> (as shown in the diagram) and measure the <u>volume of CO$_2$ produced</u> in a <u>set amount of time</u> (e.g. 10 minutes).

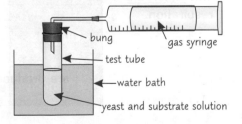
bung
gas syringe
test tube
water bath
yeast and substrate solution

5) If you <u>divide</u> the <u>volume</u> of CO$_2$ produced by the <u>time</u> taken to produce it, you can <u>calculate</u> the overall <u>rate of respiration</u>. You can then <u>repeat</u> the experiment with a <u>different substrate</u> and <u>compare</u> the two rates.

Respiration transfers energy — but this page has worn me out...

Thank goodness for respiration — transferring the energy stored in my tea and biscuits to my brain cells. Great.

Q1　Give the word equation for aerobic respiration. [2 marks]

More on Respiration

Now on to the second type of respiration — anaerobic respiration. As you're about to find out, different organisms have different ways of going about it. Makes life a tad more interesting I suppose...

Anaerobic Respiration Doesn't Use Oxygen At All

1) "Anaerobic" just means "without oxygen". It's not the best way to transfer energy from glucose because it transfers much less energy per glucose molecule than aerobic respiration — just 2 molecules of ATP are produced.

2) Anaerobic respiration takes place in the cytoplasm of animal and plant cells (and some microorganisms) when there's very little or no oxygen. For example:

> 1) Human cells — When you do really vigorous exercise your body can't supply enough oxygen to your muscle cells for aerobic respiration — they have to start respiring anaerobically as well.
>
> 2) Plant root cells — If the soil a plant's growing in becomes waterlogged there'll be no oxygen available for the roots, so the root cells will have to respire anaerobically.
>
> 3) Bacterial cells — Bacteria can get under your skin through puncture wounds caused by things like nails. There's very little oxygen under your skin, so only bacteria that can respire anaerobically can survive there.

3) The process of anaerobic respiration is slightly different in different organisms:

Animals and Some Bacteria Produce Lactic Acid

In animals and some bacteria, glucose is only partially broken down during anaerobic respiration and lactic acid is formed as a waste product. Here's the word equation:

$$glucose \longrightarrow lactic\ acid$$

Plants and Some Microorganisms Produce Ethanol and Carbon Dioxide

When plants and some microorganisms (including yeast) respire anaerobically, they produce ethanol and carbon dioxide instead of lactic acid. This is the word equation:

$$glucose \longrightarrow ethanol + carbon\ dioxide$$

Anaerobic respiration in yeast is known as fermentation.

You Need to Compare Aerobic and Anaerobic Respiration

This handy table shows the differences and similarities between aerobic and anaerobic respiration.

	Aerobic	Anaerobic
Conditions	Oxygen present	Not enough oxygen present, e.g. during vigorous exercise, in waterlogged soils
Inputs	Glucose (or another organic molecule) and oxygen	Glucose (or another organic molecule)
Outputs	Carbon dioxide and water	In animals and some bacteria — lactic acid In plants and some microorganisms (e.g. yeast) — ethanol and carbon dioxide
ATP yield	High — 32 ATP made per molecule of glucose	Much lower — 2 ATP made per molecule of glucose

My friend Anna O'Bic is rather odd — I only see her at the gym...

Make sure you know those word equations and can compare the processes of aerobic and anaerobic respiration.

Q1 Name the product(s) of anaerobic respiration in plants. [1 mark]

Q2 Why is it advantageous for organisms to respire aerobically rather than anaerobically? [1 mark]

The Cell Cycle and Mitosis

In order to survive and grow, our cells have got to be able to <u>divide</u>. And that means our DNA as well.

The Cell Cycle Makes New Cells for Growth and Repair

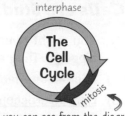

interphase

The Cell Cycle

mitosis

As you can see from the diagram, a cell spends most of its time in interphase — mitosis is a relatively small chunk of the cell cycle.

1) <u>Body cells</u> in <u>multicellular</u> organisms <u>divide</u> to produce <u>new cells</u> as part of a series of stages called the <u>cell cycle</u>. The stage of the cell cycle when the cell divides is called <u>mitosis</u>.

2) Multicellular organisms use <u>mitosis</u> to <u>grow</u> (which involves increasing the number of body cells) or to <u>replace cells</u> that have been <u>damaged</u>.

3) The end of the cell cycle results in two new cells <u>identical</u> to the <u>original</u> cell, with the <u>same number</u> of chromosomes.

4) You need to know about these two main stages of the <u>cell cycle</u>:

Interphase

1) In a cell that's not dividing, the DNA is all spread out in <u>long strings</u>.

2) Before it divides, the cell has to <u>grow</u> and <u>increase</u> the amount of <u>subcellular structures</u> such as <u>mitochondria</u> and <u>ribosomes</u>.

3) It then <u>duplicates</u> its DNA — so there's one copy for each new cell. The DNA is copied and forms <u>X-shaped</u> chromosomes. Each 'arm' of the chromosome is an <u>exact copy</u> of the other.

The left arm has the same DNA as the right arm of the chromosome.

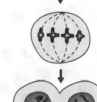

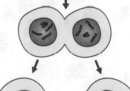

Mitosis

Once its contents and DNA have been copied, the cell is ready for <u>mitosis</u>...

4) The chromosomes <u>line up</u> at the centre of the cell and <u>cell fibres</u> pull them apart. The <u>two arms</u> of each chromosome go to <u>opposite ends</u> of the cell.

5) <u>Membranes</u> form around each of the sets of chromosomes. These become the <u>nuclei</u> of the two new cells — the <u>nucleus</u> has <u>divided</u>.

6) Lastly, the <u>cytoplasm</u> and <u>cell membrane</u> divide.

The cell has now produced <u>two new daughter cells</u>. The daughter cells contain exactly the <u>same chromosomes</u> (DNA) — they're <u>genetically identical</u>. They're also <u>genetically identical</u> to the <u>parent cell</u>.

5) You can <u>estimate</u> the <u>number of cells</u> there'll be after <u>multiple divisions</u> of a cell by mitosis. The formula you need is: <u>number of cells = 2^n</u>, where '<u>n</u>' is the <u>number of divisions</u> by mitosis.

> E.g. a scientist sees that a cell divides by mitosis <u>once every 30 minutes</u>. After <u>4 hours</u> (approx. <u>8 divisions</u>) he estimates that there'll be <u>2^8</u> = 2 × 2 × 2 × 2 × 2 × 2 × 2 × 2 = <u>256 cells</u>.

6) This is only an <u>estimate</u> though. In the example above, you can't be sure that the cells will <u>keep dividing</u> at the <u>same rate</u> for four hours (so you can't be sure that there were 8 divisions). That's because the <u>rate of cell division</u> depends on the <u>environmental conditions</u>, e.g. a <u>lack</u> of <u>food</u> could cause the rate to <u>decrease</u>. Also, some of the cells might <u>die</u>, affecting the total number left at the end.

Cancer is a Case of Uncontrolled Cell Division

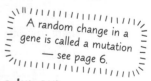

A random change in a gene is called a mutation — see page 6.

1) The <u>rate</u> at which <u>cells divide</u> by <u>mitosis</u> is controlled by the cells' <u>genes</u>.

2) If there's a <u>change</u> in one of the genes that controls cell division, a cell may start dividing <u>uncontrollably</u>. This can result in a <u>mass of abnormal cells</u> called a <u>tumour</u>.

3) If the tumour <u>invades and destroys</u> surrounding tissue it is called <u>cancer</u>. Cancer is a <u>non-communicable disease</u> (see page 24).

A cell's favourite computer game — divide and conquer...

Mitosis can seem tricky at first. But don't worry — just go through it slowly, one step at a time.

Q1   Describe what happens during the interphase stage of the cell cycle.   [3 marks]

Microscopy

Biologists <u>love microscopes</u>, which is why they're making a <u>second appearance</u> in this book...

Cells are Studied Using Microscopes

1) You might remember from page 3 that microscopes use lenses to <u>magnify</u> images (make them look bigger). They also <u>increase</u> the <u>resolution</u> of an image (the detail in which it can be seen).

2) Microscope technology has <u>developed</u> over time, allowing <u>new observations</u> to be made.

3) <u>Light microscopes</u> were invented in the 1590s. They work by passing <u>light</u> through the specimen. They let us see things like <u>nuclei</u> and <u>chloroplasts</u> and we can also use them to study <u>living cells</u>.

4) <u>Electron microscopes</u> were invented in the 1930s. They use <u>electrons</u> rather than <u>light</u>. Electron microscopes have a higher <u>magnification</u> and <u>resolution</u> than light microscopes, so they let us see much <u>smaller things</u> in <u>more detail</u> like the <u>internal structure</u> of mitochondria and chloroplasts.

5) This has given us a much <u>greater understanding</u> of <u>how cells work</u>. E.g. it's allowed scientists to develop explanations about how the internal structures of mitochondria and chloroplasts relate to their <u>functions</u> in <u>respiration</u> and <u>photosynthesis</u>. However, electron microscopes can't be used to view living cells.

You can Observe Stages of Mitosis Using a Light Microscope

PRACTICAL

1) You might remember how to use a <u>light microscope</u> to <u>observe cells</u> from <u>Chapter B1</u> — if not, have a flick back to page 3.

2) <u>Chromosomes</u> can be <u>stained</u> so you can see them under a microscope. This means you can watch what happens to them <u>during mitosis</u> — and it makes high-adrenaline viewing, I can tell you.

3) These are some <u>cells</u> from a <u>plant root tip</u> shown under a light microscope at different stages of the <u>cell cycle</u> and <u>mitosis</u>.

4) The cells are being viewed on a 'squash' microscope slide. In other words, they've been deliberately squashed beneath the cover slip. This makes it easier to see the chromosomes.

5) Cells are taken from the root <u>tip</u> as that's where <u>most cell division happens</u> in the root.

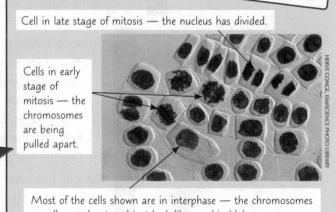

Cell in late stage of mitosis — the nucleus has divided.

Cells in early stage of mitosis — the chromosomes are being pulled apart.

Most of the cells shown are in interphase — the chromosomes are all spread out and just look like one big blob.

You Can Estimate the Size of Cells Under a Microscope

There are some clever <u>calculations</u> you can do to work out the <u>exact size</u> of cells under the microscope — in fact, you can find out how to do them on the next page. But sometimes, to make life easier, you might just want to <u>estimate</u> the <u>relative sizes</u> of two cells.

 EXAMPLE:

Look at the plant cells on the right.
Estimate how many times bigger Cell 2 is than Cell 1.

There are different ways to answer this.

1) If you compare the cells, you can see that Cell 2 is about <u>twice the height</u> and <u>twice the width</u> of Cell 1. So Cell 2 is roughly <u>2 x</u> as <u>tall</u> or <u>wide</u> as Cell 1.

2) So you can estimate that the <u>area</u> of Cell 2 is 2^2 or <u>4 x</u> as great as Cell 1, and the <u>volume</u> is 2^3 or <u>8 x</u> as great.

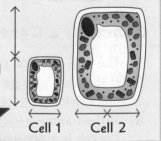

Cell 1　　Cell 2

I take my microscope everywhere — good job it's a light one...

We're not done with microscopy yet I'm afraid. Do this question, then move on to the next page.

Q1　Explain how electron microscopes have given us a greater understanding of how cells work.　[2 marks]

More Microscopy

Sometimes you need to do a bit of <u>maths</u> with microscope images. It's time to get your <u>numbers head on</u>...

Magnification is How Many Times Bigger the Image is

What are you looking at?

1) If you know the <u>power</u> of the lenses used by a microscope to view an image, you can work out the <u>total magnification</u> of the image using this simple formula:

> total magnification = eyepiece lens magnification × objective lens magnification

2) For example, the <u>total magnification</u> of an image viewed with an <u>eyepiece lens</u> magnification of <u>× 10</u> and an <u>objective lens</u> magnification of <u>× 40</u> would be 10 × 40 = <u>× 400</u>.

3) If you don't know which lenses were used, you can still work out the magnification of an image as long as you can <u>measure the image</u> and know the <u>actual size of the specimen</u>. This is the <u>formula</u> you need:

$$\text{magnification} = \frac{\text{measured size}}{\text{actual size}}$$

— Both measurements should have the same units. If they don't, you'll need to convert them first (see below).

4) If you're working out the <u>measured size</u> or the <u>actual size</u> of the object, you can rearrange the equation using the <u>formula triangle</u>. <u>Cover up</u> the thing you're trying to find. The parts you can <u>still see</u> are the formula you need to use.

measured size / magnification × actual size

You Might Need to Work With Numbers in Standard Form and Convert Units

1) Because microscopes can see such <u>tiny objects</u>, sometimes it's useful to write figures in <u>standard form</u>.

2) This is where you write a number in the form $\underline{A \times 10^n}$ — where '<u>A</u>' is a number <u>between 1 and 10</u>, and '<u>n</u>' is the <u>number of places</u> the <u>decimal point</u> moves. '<u>n</u>' is <u>positive</u> for numbers <u>greater than 1</u> and <u>negative</u> for numbers <u>less than 1</u>. E.g. 0.017 is written 1.7×10^{-2} in standard form.

3) Standard form is useful for writing <u>very big</u> or <u>very small numbers</u> in a more <u>manageable way</u>.

4) You can also use <u>different units</u> to express very big or very small numbers. E.g. <u>0.0007 m</u> could be written as <u>0.7 mm</u>. The <u>table</u> below shows you how to <u>convert between different units</u>. The right hand column of the table shows you how each unit can be expressed as a <u>metre</u> in <u>standard form</u> — the more negative the power of 10, the smaller the value. So, for example, 1 mm = 0.001 m and 1 pm = 0.000000000001 m. (That's tiny!)

To convert

Unit	To convert	In standard form:
Millimetre (mm)	÷1000	$\times 10^{-3}$ m
Micrometre (μm)	÷1000	$\times 10^{-6}$ m
Nanometre (nm)	÷1000	$\times 10^{-9}$ m
Picometre (pm)		$\times 10^{-12}$ m

× 1000
× 1000
× 1000

5) Here's an example of a <u>calculation</u> in standard form:

EXAMPLE: A specimen is 5×10^{-6} m wide. Calculate the width of the image of the specimen under a magnification of × 100. Give your answer in standard form.

1) <u>Rearrange</u> the magnification formula — the width of the image is the <u>measured size</u>, so cover up measured size on the <u>formula triangle</u>.

2) Fill in the <u>values</u> you know.

3) Write out the values <u>in full</u> (i.e. don't use standard form).

4) Carry out the calculation and then <u>convert back</u> into standard form.

measured size = magnification × actual size

measured size = 100 × (5×10^{-6} m)

= 100 × 0.000005 m

= 0.0005 m

= 5×10^{-4} m

Note: 0.0005 m could also be written as 0.5 mm or 500 μm.

Mi-cros-copy — when my twin gets annoyed...

If you've got a scientific calculator, you can put standard form numbers into your calculator using the 'EXP' or the '×10^x' button. For example, enter 2.67×10^{15} by pressing 2.67 then 'EXP' or '10^x', then 15. Easy.

Q1 Calculate the actual length of a cell which has a measured size of 7×10^{-1} mm under a magnification of × 400. Write your answer in μm. [3 marks]

Sexual Reproduction and Meiosis

Ever wondered why you look <u>like</u> your <u>family members</u>, but <u>not exactly the same</u>? Well today's your lucky day.

Sexual Reproduction Produces Genetically Different Cells

1) <u>Sexual reproduction</u> is where genetic information from <u>two</u> organisms (a <u>father</u> and a <u>mother</u>) is combined to produce offspring which are <u>genetically different</u> to either parent.

2) In <u>sexual reproduction</u>, the father and mother produce <u>gametes</u> — in animals these are <u>sperm</u> and <u>egg cells</u>.

3) Gametes only contain <u>half the number</u> of <u>chromosomes</u> of normal cells (see page 4).

4) At <u>fertilisation</u>, a male gamete <u>fuses</u> with a female gamete to produce a <u>fertilised egg</u>, known as a <u>zygote</u>. Chromosomes from the mother <u>pair up</u> with chromosomes from the father, so the zygote ends up with the <u>full set</u> of chromosomes.

5) The zygote then undergoes <u>cell division</u> (by mitosis — see p.59) and develops into an <u>embryo</u>.

6) The embryo <u>inherits characteristics</u> from <u>both parents</u> as it's received a <u>mixture of chromosomes</u> (and therefore <u>genes</u>) from its mum and its dad.

A human body cell nucleus contains 46 chromosomes — a human gamete has 23 chromosomes.

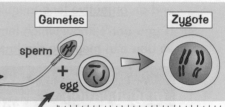

This diagram isn't drawn to scale — egg cells are actually much bigger than sperm cells. That's because they contain all the subcellular structures and nutrients needed for the zygote to grow and develop.

Gametes are Produced by Meiosis

Meiosis is a type of <u>cell division</u>. It produces <u>genetically different</u> cells with <u>half the chromosomes</u> of the original cell. In humans, meiosis <u>only</u> happens in the <u>reproductive organs</u> (ovaries and testes).

Division 1

1) Before meiosis can begin, the cell goes through <u>interphase</u>. During this period it <u>duplicates</u> its <u>DNA</u> (so there's enough for each new cell). One arm of each X-shaped chromosome is an <u>exact copy</u> of the other arm.

2) In the <u>first division</u> in meiosis (there are two divisions) the chromosomes <u>line up</u> in pairs in the centre of the cell. One chromosome in each pair came from the organism's mother and one came from its father.

3) The <u>pairs</u> are then <u>pulled apart</u>, so each new cell ends up with <u>one chromosome</u> from each pair. <u>Some</u> of the father's chromosomes and <u>some</u> of the mother's chromosomes go into each new cell.

4) This means the <u>chromosome number</u> of <u>each new cell</u> will be <u>half</u> that of the original cell. Each new cell will also have a <u>mixture</u> of the mother's and father's chromosomes. Mixing up the genes like this is <u>really important</u> — it creates <u>genetic variation</u> in the offspring (i.e. each offspring will have a different mixture of alleles.

Division 2

5) In the <u>second division</u> the chromosomes <u>line up</u> again in the centre of the cell. It's a lot like mitosis. The <u>arms</u> of the chromosomes are <u>pulled apart</u>.

6) You get <u>four gametes</u> — each only has a <u>single set</u> of chromosomes. The gametes are all <u>genetically different</u>.

This cell has duplicated each chromosome — each arm of the X-shape is identical.

chromosome pair

Half of the chromosomes in the starting cell were inherited from the organism's father (blue) and half from its mother (red).

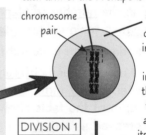

DIVISION 1

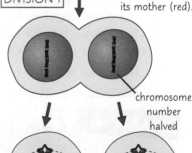

chromosome number halved

DIVISION 2

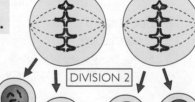

Identical twins are genetically identical because they come from a single zygote that splits in two, then develops into two separate embryos.

Now that I have your undivided attention...

Remember — in humans, meiosis only occurs in the reproductive organs, when gametes are made.

Q1   Explain why gametes need to have half the number of chromosomes of a normal body cell.   [2 marks]

Stem Cells

Your body is made up of all sorts of weird and wonderful cells. This page tells you where they all came from...

Stem Cells can Differentiate into Different Types of Cells

1) To start with, the cells in an embryo are all the same. They're called embryonic stem cells.

2) Embryonic stem cells are unspecialised. This means they're able to divide to produce any type of specialised cell (e.g. blood cells, nerve cells). In humans, all the cells in the embryo are unspecialised up to the eight cell stage.

3) The process of stem cells becoming specialised is called differentiation. After the eight cell stage, most of the stem cells in a human embryo start to differentiate. This allows the embryo to grow and develop tissues — these are groups of specialised cells working together with a particular function.

4) Adult humans only have stem cells in certain places like the bone marrow. Adult stem cells can become specialised, but they can only differentiate into certain types of cell. They are important in replacing dead cells, e.g. in making new red blood cells.

5) All body cells contain the same genes, but in specialised cells most of the genes are not active — so the cells only produce the specific proteins they need. Stem cells can switch any gene on or off during their development — the genes that are active (on) produce the proteins that determine the type of specialised cell a stem cell will become.

Meristems Contain Plant Stem Cells

1) In plants, the only cells that divide by mitosis (see p.59) are found in plant tissues called meristems.

2) Meristem tissue is found in the areas of a plant that are growing, e.g. the tips of the roots and shoots.

3) Meristems produce unspecialised cells that are able to divide and form any cell type in the plant — they act like embryonic stem cells. But unlike human stem cells, these cells can differentiate to generate any type of cell for as long as the plant lives.

4) The unspecialised cells go on to form specialised tissues like xylem and phloem (see p.40).

A merry stem.

Stem Cells Can be Used in Medicine

1) Scientists have experimented with extracting stem cells from very early human embryos and growing them. Under certain conditions the stem cells can be stimulated to differentiate into specialised cells.

2) It might be possible to use stem cells to create specialised cells to replace those which have been damaged by disease or injury, e.g. new cardiac muscle cells could be transplanted into someone with heart disease. This potential for new cures is the reason for the huge scientific interest in stem cells.

3) Before this can happen, a lot of research needs to be done. There are many potential risks which scientists need to learn more about. For example:

- Tumour development — stem cells divide very quickly. If scientists are unable to control the rate at which the transplanted cells divide inside a patient, a tumour may develop (see page 59).

- Disease transmission — viruses live inside cells. If donor stem cells are infected with a virus and this isn't picked up, the virus could be passed on to the recipient and so make them sicker.

4) The use of embryonic stem cells in this way also raises ethical issues. For example, some people argue that human embryos shouldn't be used to provide stem cells because the embryo gets destroyed and each one is a potential human life. But others think that the aim of curing patients who are suffering should be more important than the potential life of the embryos.

5) It's such a tricky issue that the use of human embryonic stem cells in scientific research and medicine is regulated by the government in most countries, including the UK.

Cheery cells, those merry-stems...

Turns out stem cells are pretty nifty. Now, let's see if you're specialised to answer this question...

Q1   If the tip is cut off a plant shoot, the tip can be used to grow a whole new plant. Suggest why.   [3 marks]

Plant Growth

Like humans (see page 74), <u>plants</u> produce chemical messengers called <u>hormones</u>.

Auxins are Plant Growth Hormones

1) <u>Auxins</u> are <u>plant hormones</u> which control and coordinate <u>growth</u> at the <u>tips</u> of <u>shoots</u> and <u>roots</u>. They move through the plant in <u>solution</u> (dissolved in water).

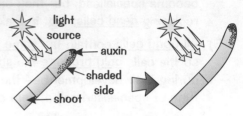

2) Auxin is produced in the <u>tips</u> and <u>diffuses backwards</u> to stimulate the <u>cells to elongate</u> (grow), which occurs in the cells <u>just behind</u> the tips.

3) Auxin <u>promotes</u> growth in the <u>shoot</u>, but actually <u>inhibits</u> growth in the <u>root</u>.

4) Auxins are involved in the <u>growth</u> responses of plants to <u>light</u> (phototropism) and <u>gravity</u> (gravitropism).

Auxins Change the Direction of Root and Shoot Growth

<u>SHOOTS ARE POSITIVELY PHOTOTROPIC</u> (grow towards light)

1) When a <u>shoot tip</u> is exposed to <u>light</u>, it accumulates <u>more auxin</u> on the side that's in the <u>shade</u> than the side that's in the <u>light</u>.

2) This makes the cells grow (elongate) <u>faster</u> on the <u>shaded side</u>, so the shoot bends <u>towards</u> the light.

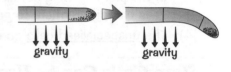

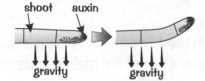

<u>SHOOTS ARE NEGATIVELY GRAVITROPIC</u> (grow away from gravity)

1) When a <u>shoot</u> is growing sideways, <u>gravity</u> produces an unequal distribution of auxin in the tip, with <u>more auxin</u> on the <u>lower side</u>.

2) This causes the lower side to grow <u>faster</u>, bending the shoot <u>upwards</u>.

<u>ROOTS ARE POSITIVELY GRAVITROPIC</u> (grow towards gravity)

1) A <u>root</u> growing sideways will also have more auxin on its <u>lower side</u>.

2) But in a root the <u>extra</u> auxin <u>inhibits</u> growth. This means the cells on <u>top</u> elongate faster, and the root bends <u>downwards</u>.

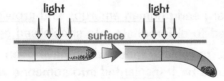

<u>ROOTS ARE NEGATIVELY PHOTOTROPIC</u> (grow away from light)

1) If a <u>root</u> starts being exposed to some <u>light</u>, <u>more auxin</u> accumulates on the more <u>shaded</u> side.

2) The auxin <u>inhibits</u> cell elongation on the shaded side, so the root bends <u>downwards</u>, back into the ground.

Phototropism and gravitropism <u>increase</u> a plant's <u>chance of survival</u>. For example, by <u>growing towards</u> the <u>light</u>, a plant shoot is able to <u>absorb more light</u> for <u>photosynthesis</u>. And by <u>growing downwards</u>, a plant root is more likely to anchor itself into the soil and find <u>water</u> and <u>minerals</u>.

Plant Hormones Are Used to Help Cuttings Grow Roots

1) A <u>cutting</u> is part of a plant that has been <u>cut off it</u>, like the end of a branch with a few leaves on it.

2) Normally, if you stick cuttings in the soil they <u>won't grow</u>, but if you add <u>rooting powder</u>, which contains <u>auxins</u>, they will <u>produce roots</u> rapidly and start growing as <u>new plants</u>.

3) This enables growers to produce lots of <u>clones</u> (exact copies) of a really good plant <u>very quickly</u>.

4) It's just one example of humans <u>exploiting</u> plant hormones by using them to trigger responses in plants that are <u>beneficial</u> to us. There are some more examples of this on the next page.

A plant auxin to a bar — 'ouch'...

Quite a bit to learn on this page — cover it up and scribble it all down till you're confident you know it all.

Q1   Name a part of a plant that is positively phototropic.   [1 mark]

More on Plant Growth

First up, a <u>nice little experiment</u>. Then there are some <u>more plant hormones</u> for you to learn about.

You Can Investigate the Role of Auxins in Phototropism

For these experiments you need some <u>shoots</u> with <u>coleoptiles</u>, e.g. oats, grasses.

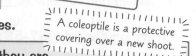
A coleoptile is a protective covering over a new shoot.

1) Plant <u>three lots</u> of three shoots in damp soil. Leave one lot of shoots as they are. Put <u>foil caps</u> on the <u>tips</u> of another lot of shoots. <u>Wrap foil</u> around the <u>bases</u> of the final lot of shoots.

2) Put each group of shoots in a <u>cardboard box</u> with a <u>hole in one side</u>. Put a <u>light source</u> next to the hole.

3) <u>Leave</u> the shoots for a <u>few days</u>. You should notice that:

- The shoots <u>without any foil</u> have <u>grown towards</u> the <u>light</u>.
- The shoots with <u>foil caps</u> have <u>grown straight upwards</u>.
- The shoots with <u>foil</u> around their <u>bases</u> have grown <u>towards</u> the <u>light</u>.

4) This experiment shows that growth towards the light is <u>only prevented</u> when the <u>shoot tips</u> are <u>covered</u>, so the <u>auxins</u> must be <u>active</u> in the <u>tip</u>.

light source — foil cap — foil round base

Other Hormones Are Also Involved in Plant Growth

Gibberellins Control Germination and Flowering

1) Lots of seeds <u>won't germinate</u> (start growing) until they've been through <u>certain conditions</u> (e.g. a period of <u>cold</u> or of <u>dryness</u>). This is called <u>dormancy</u>.

2) <u>Gibberellins</u> are plant hormones that break this dormancy and allow the seeds to <u>germinate</u>.

3) Commercial growers can <u>treat seeds</u> with gibberellins to make them germinate at <u>times of year</u> when they <u>wouldn't</u> normally. It also helps to make sure <u>all</u> the seeds in a batch germinate at the <u>same time</u>.

4) Gibberellins also trigger a plant response called '<u>bolting</u>' in response to a <u>cold</u> spell or <u>lack of water</u>. This is when a plant produces <u>lots of flowers</u> in an attempt to <u>reproduce</u> before it <u>dies</u>.

5) This means commercial growers can use gibberellins to make plants <u>flower earlier</u> than they would usually do so, or under <u>conditions</u> in which they wouldn't usually flower.

Ethene Stimulates Shedding of Leaves and Ripening of Fruit

1) <u>Ethene</u> is produced by <u>aging leaves</u>. It stimulates cells that connect the leaf to the rest of the plant to <u>expand</u> — this <u>breaks the cell walls</u> and causes the leaf to <u>fall off the plant</u>.

2) Commercial growers sometimes use ethene to <u>remove the leaves</u> from a crop (e.g. <u>cotton</u>) <u>before</u> it's <u>harvested</u>. This makes collecting the <u>seeds</u> or <u>fruits</u> easier.

3) Ethene also <u>stimulates enzymes</u> that cause <u>fruit to ripen</u>.

4) This means ethene can be used to control the ripening of fruits either while they are still on the plant, or during <u>transport</u> to the shops. The fruit is picked while it's still <u>unripe</u> (and therefore firmer and <u>less easily damaged</u>) and <u>ethene gas</u> is then <u>added</u>. The fruit then will ripen on the way to the supermarket and be <u>perfect</u> just as it reaches the shelves.

You will germinate when I SAY you can — and NOT BEFORE...

Make sure you learn the effects of auxins, gibberellin and ethene and how we can use them to our advantage.

Q1   Give two ways in which gibberellin affects the natural growth and development of plants.   [2 marks]

Revision Questions for Chapter B4

Hurrah. It's the <u>end</u> of <u>Chapter B4</u>. Better get this one last page over with.

*   Try these questions and <u>tick off each one</u> when you <u>get it right</u>.
*   When you've done <u>all the questions</u> for a topic and are <u>completely happy</u> with it, tick off the topic.

<u>Respiration (p.57-58)</u> ☐

1)   What is respiration?
2)   Is respiration an exothermic or an endothermic reaction?
3)   Name the type of respiration that requires oxygen.
4)   Briefly describe an experiment to investigate the effect of different substrates on the rate of respiration in yeast.
5)   Describe a situation when: a) a plant root would have to respire anaerobically.
                                                   b) a bacterium would have to respire anaerobically.
6)   Give an example of when lactic acid would be produced as a product of respiration.
7)   Which form of respiration has a greater ATP yield per glucose molecule?

<u>The Cell Cycle, Mitosis and Microscopy (p.59-61)</u> ☑

8)   What is the cell cycle?
9)   What is mitosis used for by multicellular organisms?
10) What major illness can result from uncontrolled cell division?
11) Give an advantage of electron microscopes over light microscopes.
12) Why is it necessary to squash a plant root tip if you want to view the cells dividing by mitosis under a light microscope?
13) Write the formula you would use to find the actual size of a specimen using the magnification used and the measured size of the image seen through a microscope lens.
14) Describe how you would convert a measurement from mm to μm.
15) Which unit can be expressed in standard form as $\times 10^{-12}$ m?

<u>Sexual Reproduction, Meiosis and Stem Cells (p.62-63)</u> ☑

16) Name the gametes in humans.
17) Describe how gametes are formed by meiosis.
18) What is a stem cell?
19) How are embryonic stem cells different to adult stem cells?
20) Which parts of a plant contain stem cells?
21) What are the potential benefits of stem cells being used in medicine?

<u>Plant Growth (p.64-65)</u> ☑

22) What are auxins?
23) Shoots are positively phototropic. What does this mean?
24) Roots are positively gravitropic. Explain the role of auxin in this response.
25) Explain how rooting powders work.
26) Briefly describe an experiment you could do to investigate the role of auxins in plant growth.
27) Name a plant hormone that controls fruit ripening.

Exchange of Materials

As you might remember from Chapter B3, all organisms need to <u>exchange</u> things with their <u>environment</u>...

Humans Exchange Substances with their Environment

Like all organisms, humans and other animals must <u>take in</u> the substances they need from the environment and <u>get rid</u> of any <u>waste products</u>. For example:

There's more on diffusion and osmosis on p.37.

- Cells need <u>oxygen</u> for <u>aerobic respiration</u> (see p.57), which produces <u>carbon dioxide</u> as a waste product. These two <u>gases</u> move between <u>cells</u> and the <u>environment</u> by <u>diffusion</u>.
- <u>Water</u> is needed for many chemical reactions. It's taken up by cells by <u>osmosis</u>. Dissolved <u>food molecules</u> (the products of digestion, e.g. glucose and amino acids) diffuse along with it. These are then used in <u>synthesis reactions</u> (see p.51).

CO_2 and urea need to be removed before they reach toxic levels.

- <u>Urea</u> (a waste product from the breakdown of proteins in the liver) diffuses from <u>cells</u> into the <u>blood plasma</u>. It is then <u>filtered out</u> of the blood by the <u>kidneys</u> and <u>excreted</u> as <u>urine</u>.

You Can Compare Surface Area to Volume Ratios

How <u>easy</u> it is for an organism to exchange substances with its environment depends on the organism's <u>surface area to volume ratio</u> (<u>SA : V</u>). A ratio shows <u>how big</u> one value is <u>compared</u> to another. The <u>larger</u> an organism is, the <u>smaller</u> its surface area is compared to its volume:

A hippo can be represented by a 2 cm × 4 cm × 4 cm block.

The <u>area</u> of a surface is found by the equation: LENGTH × WIDTH
So the hippo's <u>total surface area</u> is:

      (4 × 4) × 2 (top and bottom surfaces of block)
    + (4 × 2) × 4 (four sides of the block)
    = 64 cm².

The <u>volume</u> of a block is found by the equation: LENGTH × WIDTH × HEIGHT
So the hippo's <u>volume</u> is 4 × 4 × 2 = 32 cm³.

The surface area to volume ratio of the hippo can be written as <u>64 : 32</u>.
To get the ratio in the form <u>n : 1</u>, <u>divide both sides</u> of the ratio by the <u>volume</u>.
So the surface area to volume ratio of the hippo is <u>2 : 1</u>.

A mouse can be represented by a 1 cm × 1 cm × 1 cm block.
Its <u>surface area</u> is (1 × 1) × 6 = 6 cm².
Its <u>volume</u> is 1 × 1 × 1 = 1 cm³.
So the surface area to volume ratio of the mouse is <u>6 : 1</u>.

The cube mouse's surface area is <u>six</u> times its volume, but the cube hippo's surface area is only <u>twice</u> its volume. So the <u>mouse</u> has a <u>larger</u> surface area compared to its volume.

Multicellular Organisms Need Exchange Surfaces

1) <u>Multicellular organisms</u> have relatively <u>small</u> surface area to volume ratios, which makes <u>diffusion</u> to and from cells deep within their bodies <u>slow</u>. This makes it difficult to exchange <u>enough substances</u> to supply their <u>entire volume</u> across their outside surface alone.

2) To get around this, multicellular organisms usually have <u>specialised exchange surfaces</u> to <u>increase</u> their <u>SA : V</u> and therefore the <u>rate</u> at which substances are able to diffuse (see next page for more). Organisms also tend to have a <u>mass transport system</u> (e.g. a circulatory system) to <u>move substances</u> around the body — this <u>shortens</u> the <u>distance</u> these substances have to diffuse to and from cells.

Some small multicellular organisms, e.g. earthworms, have a big enough SA : V that they don't need specialised exchange surfaces.

3) All of the movement into, out of and around the <u>human body</u> is dependent on the <u>gaseous exchange</u>, <u>circulatory</u>, <u>digestive</u> and <u>excretory systems</u> all <u>working together</u>.

Not that I'm endorsing putting animals in boxes...

Have a go at this question to make sure you understand how to calculate surface area to volume ratios.

Q1   A bacterial cell can be represented by a 1 μm × 1 μm × 4 μm block. Calculate the cell's surface area to volume ratio. Give your ratio in its simplest whole number form.   **[3 marks]**

Human Exchange Surfaces

This page is about how exchange surfaces in humans are <u>adapted</u> so that substances can move through them by <u>diffusion</u>, <u>osmosis</u> and <u>active transport</u>. If you need to look over these processes, flick back to page 37.

O_2 and CO_2 Diffuse Between Alveoli and Capillaries

Remember, human cells are animal cells.

1) The job of the <u>lungs</u> is to transfer <u>oxygen</u> to the <u>blood</u> and to remove <u>waste carbon dioxide</u> from it.

2) To do this, the lungs contain millions of little air sacs called <u>alveoli</u> where <u>gas exchange</u> takes place.

3) The alveoli are surrounded by a network of tiny blood vessels called <u>capillaries</u>.

4) <u>Oxygen</u> (O_2) diffuses from the <u>air</u> in the <u>alveoli</u> into the <u>blood</u> in the <u>capillaries</u>. <u>Carbon dioxide</u> (CO_2) diffuses in the <u>opposite direction</u>.

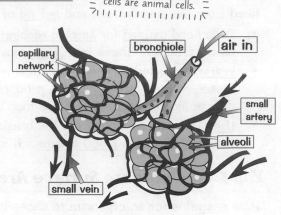

Blue = blood with carbon dioxide.
Red = blood with oxygen.

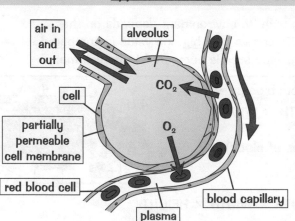

5) The alveoli are specialised to maximise the <u>rate of diffusion</u> of O_2 and CO_2. They have:

- An <u>enormous surface area</u> (about 75 m² in humans).
- A <u>moist lining</u> for dissolving gases.
- Very <u>thin walls</u> (consisting of cells with <u>partially permeable</u> cell membranes).
- A <u>good blood supply</u>.

Dissolved Food and Water are Absorbed in the Digestive System

1) <u>Digested food</u> is absorbed in the <u>small intestine</u>. The inside of the small intestine is covered in millions and millions of tiny little projections called <u>villi</u>.

2) Villi <u>increase</u> the <u>surface area</u> in a big way so that digested food is quickly <u>absorbed</u> into the <u>blood</u> by <u>active transport</u> and <u>diffusion</u>. For example:

- When there's a <u>higher concentration</u> of <u>glucose</u> in the intestine, it <u>diffuses</u> naturally <u>into the blood</u>.
- When there's a <u>lower concentration</u> of glucose in the intestine, it is <u>actively transported</u> into the blood. This allows glucose to be taken into the blood, despite the fact that the concentration gradient is the wrong way.

3) Villi have a <u>single</u> layer of surface cells to assist quick absorption. Like all cells, they have <u>partially permeable cell membranes</u>, which regulate the movement of substances across them. Villi also have a very good <u>blood supply</u> to assist <u>quick absorption</u>.

4) <u>Water</u> is <u>absorbed</u> into the blood from the <u>large intestine</u> by <u>osmosis</u>.

Al Veoli — the Italian gas man...

Here's a little fact that needs wedging firmly into your brain — a big surface area means a faster rate of diffusion.

Q1   Give one way in which alveoli are adapted for gas exchange.   [1 mark]

The Circulatory System

As you saw on page 67, multicellular organisms need transport systems to move substances around effectively. In humans, it's the job of the circulatory system. My heart's all of a flutter just thinking about it...

The DOUBLE Circulatory System, Actually

The circulatory system is made up of the heart, blood vessels and blood. Humans and other mammals have a double circulatory system — two circuits joined together:

1) In the first one, the heart pumps deoxygenated blood to the alveoli in the lungs to take in oxygen. The oxygenated blood then returns to the heart.

2) In the second one, the heart pumps oxygenated blood around all the other organs of the body (see right). Here, the blood gives up its oxygen at the body cells. The deoxygenated blood then returns to the heart to be pumped out to the lungs again.

3) As it is pumped around the body, the blood also travels through blood vessels near exchange surfaces — including the villi (where it picks up food molecules and water) and the kidneys (where it is filtered and urea is removed).

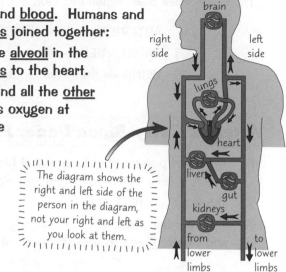

The diagram shows the right and left side of the person in the diagram, not your right and left as you look at them.

The Heart Pumps Blood Around The Body

1) The heart uses its four chambers (right and left atria and ventricles) to pump blood around.

2) The heart has valves to make sure that blood flows in the right direction. When the ventricles contract, the valves to the atria close and the valves to the blood vessels open. This prevents backflow (when the blood flows backwards).

Atria is plural. Atrium is when there is just one.

1) Blood flows into the two atria from the vena cava and the pulmonary vein.

2) The atria contract, pushing the blood into the ventricles.

3) The ventricles contract, forcing the blood into the pulmonary artery and the aorta, and out of the heart.

4) The blood then flows to the organs, including the lungs, through arteries, and returns through veins (see next page).

5) The atria fill again and the whole cycle starts over.

• The left ventricle has a much thicker wall than the right ventricle. It needs the greater pressure generated by the thicker muscle because it has to pump blood around the whole body, whereas the right ventricle only has to pump it to the lungs.

• The heart is made up of cardiac muscle. Cardiac muscle cells contain loads of mitochondria to provide them with ATP. This releases the energy needed for the muscle to contract.

• Blood is supplied to the cardiac muscle by two coronary arteries, which branch from the base of the aorta. They allow the oxygen and glucose needed for the heart cells to respire to diffuse through the thick walls of the heart.

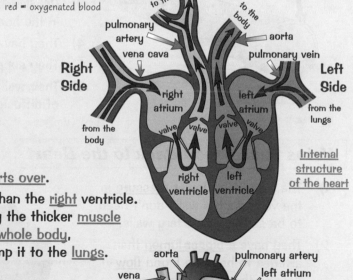

blue = deoxygenated blood
red = oxygenated blood

Internal structure of the heart

External structure of the heart

Okay — let's get to the heart of the matter...

Make sure you learn the names of the different parts of the heart and all the blood vessels that are attached to it.

Q1   Which chamber of the heart pumps deoxygenated blood to the lungs?   [1 mark]

Blood Vessels

If you want to know more about the <u>circulatory system</u> you're in luck. Because here's a whole extra page.

Blood Vessels are Designed for Their Function

There are three main types of blood vessel:

> 1) **ARTERIES** — these carry the blood <u>away</u> from the heart.
>
> 2) **CAPILLARIES** — these are involved in the <u>exchange</u> of <u>materials</u> at the tissues.
>
> 3) **VEINS** — these carry the blood <u>to</u> the heart.

Arteries Carry Blood Under Pressure

1) The heart pumps the blood out at <u>high pressure</u> so the artery walls are <u>strong</u> and <u>elastic</u>.

2) The walls are <u>thick</u> compared to the size of the <u>lumen</u>.

3) They contain thick layers of <u>muscle</u> to make them <u>strong</u>, and <u>elastic fibres</u> to allow them to stretch and <u>spring back</u>.

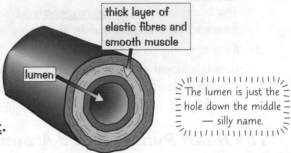

thick layer of elastic fibres and smooth muscle

lumen

The lumen is just the hole down the middle — silly name.

Capillaries are Really Small

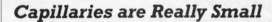
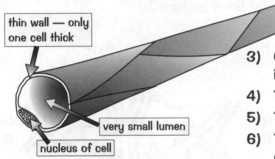

thin wall — only one cell thick

very small lumen

nucleus of cell

1) Capillaries are really <u>tiny</u> — too small to see.

2) <u>Networks of capillaries</u> in tissue are called <u>capillary beds</u>.

3) Capillaries carry the blood <u>really close</u> to <u>every cell</u> in the body to <u>exchange substances</u> with them.

4) They have <u>permeable</u> walls, so substances can <u>diffuse</u> in and out.

5) They supply <u>food</u> and <u>oxygen</u>, and take away <u>waste</u> like CO_2.

6) Their walls are usually <u>only one cell thick</u>. This <u>increases</u> the rate of diffusion by <u>decreasing</u> the <u>distance</u> over which it occurs.

Veins Take Blood Back to the Heart

1) The blood is at <u>lower pressure</u> in the veins so the walls don't need to be as <u>thick</u> as artery walls.

2) They have a <u>bigger lumen</u> than arteries to help the blood <u>flow</u> despite the lower pressure.

3) They also have <u>valves</u> to help keep the blood flowing in the <u>right direction</u>.

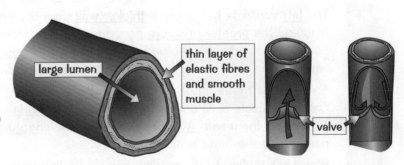

large lumen

thin layer of elastic fibres and smooth muscle

valve

Learn this page — don't struggle in vein...

Here's an interesting fact for you — your body contains about 60 000 miles of blood vessels. That's about six times the distance from London to Sydney in Australia. Of course, capillaries are really tiny, which is how such a massive amount of them can fit in your body — they can only be seen with a microscope.

Q1   Describe how veins are adapted to carry blood back to the heart.   [2 marks]

Q2   Explain how capillaries are adapted to their function.   [3 marks]

Blood

Now that we've looked at blood vessels, it's time to look at the wonders of <u>blood</u> itself.
(Hmmm — is it me, or is this starting to sound a tiny bit like a lecture for <u>vampires</u>...)

Blood Acts as a Transport System

1) Blood is a <u>tissue</u>, consisting of many similar cells working together.
2) These cells are <u>red blood cells</u>, <u>white blood cells</u> and <u>platelets</u>, and they're suspended in a liquid called <u>plasma</u>.
3) This page is all about <u>plasma</u> and <u>red blood cells</u> — the bits of the blood responsible for <u>transporting substances</u> around the body.

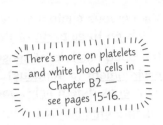
There's more on platelets and white blood cells in Chapter B2 — see pages 15-16.

Plasma is the Liquid Bit of Blood

It's basically blood minus the blood cells. Plasma is a pale yellow liquid which <u>carries just about everything</u> that needs transporting around your body:

1) <u>Red blood cells</u> (see below), <u>white blood cells</u>, and <u>platelets</u>.
2) <u>Water</u>.
3) Digested <u>food products</u> like <u>glucose</u> and <u>amino acids</u> from the small intestine to all the body cells.
4) <u>Carbon dioxide</u> from the body cells to the lungs.
5) <u>Urea</u> from the liver to the kidneys (where it's removed in the urine).
6) <u>Hormones</u> — these act like chemical messengers (see p.74).
7) <u>Antibodies</u> — these are proteins involved in the body's immune response (see p.16).

Red Blood Cells Have the Job of Carrying Oxygen

Red blood cells transport <u>oxygen</u> from the <u>lungs</u> to <u>all</u> the cells in the body.
The <u>structure</u> of a red blood cell is adapted to its <u>function</u>:

1) Red blood cells are <u>small</u> and have a <u>biconcave disc shape</u> to give a <u>large surface area to volume ratio</u>. This <u>increases</u> the <u>rate</u> at which <u>oxygen</u> can <u>diffuse</u> into and out of the cell.
2) They are packed with <u>haemoglobin</u>, which is what gives the cells a red <u>colour</u> — it contains a lot of <u>iron</u>. In the lungs, haemoglobin <u>combines with oxygen</u> to become <u>oxyhaemoglobin</u>. In body tissues, the reverse happens to <u>release oxygen to the cells</u>.
3) Red blood cells <u>don't</u> have a <u>nucleus</u> — this frees up <u>space</u> for more haemoglobin, so they can carry more oxygen.
4) As they are <u>small</u> and very <u>flexible</u> they can easily pass through the <u>tiny capillaries</u> close to the body cells.

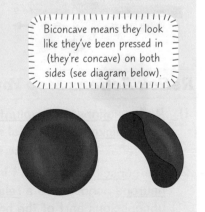
Biconcave means they look like they've been pressed in (they're concave) on both sides (see diagram below).

A <u>low number</u> of red blood cells can make you feel <u>tired</u>. This is because <u>less oxygen</u> can be transported around the body, and so there is <u>less aerobic respiration</u> taking place to produce <u>ATP</u> (see p.57).

Blood's other function is to let you know you're bleeding...

Every single drop contains millions of red blood cells — all of them perfectly designed for carrying plenty of oxygen to where it's needed. Which right now is your brain, so you can get cracking with learning this page.

Q1   Name the substance that combines with oxygen and gives red blood cells their colour.   [1 mark]

Q2   Describe three ways in which red blood cells are adapted to carry oxygen.   [3 marks]

The Nervous System

The <u>nervous system</u> is what lets you <u>react</u> to what goes on around you, so you'd find life tough without it.

The Central Nervous System Coordinates a Response

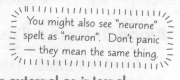
You might also see "neurone" spelt as "neuron". Don't panic — they mean the same thing.

1) The nervous system is made up of <u>neurones</u> (nerve cells), which go to <u>all parts</u> of the body.

2) The body has lots of <u>sensory receptors</u>, which can detect a <u>change in your external or internal environment</u> (a <u>stimulus</u>). Different sensory receptors detect different stimuli. For example, receptors in your <u>eyes</u> detect <u>light</u>, and receptors in your <u>skin</u> detect <u>touch</u> (pressure) and <u>temperature change</u>.

3) When a <u>stimulus</u> is detected by <u>receptors</u>, the information is sent as <u>nervous (electrical) impulses</u> along <u>sensory neurones</u> to the <u>central nervous system</u> (<u>CNS</u>).

4) The CNS consists of the <u>brain</u> and <u>spinal cord</u>.

5) The CNS <u>coordinates</u> the response (in other words, it <u>decides what to do</u> about the stimulus and tells something to do it).

6) The CNS sends information to an <u>effector</u> (<u>muscle</u> or <u>gland</u>) along a <u>motor neurone</u>. The effector then <u>responds</u> accordingly — e.g. a <u>muscle</u> may <u>contract</u> or a <u>gland</u> may <u>secrete a hormone</u>.

7) Nervous communication is very <u>fast</u>, but the responses are <u>short-lived</u> (they don't last long).

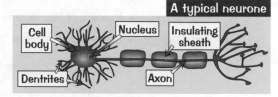

Stimulus → Receptor → Sensory neurone → CNS → Motor neurone → Effector → Response

Light receptors

Neurones Transmit Information Rapidly as Electrical Impulses

1) <u>Electrical impulses</u> are passed along the <u>axon</u> of a neurone.

2) Neurones have <u>branched endings</u> (<u>dendrites</u>) so they can <u>connect</u> with lots of other neurones.

3) Some axons are also surrounded by a <u>fatty (myelin) sheath</u>. This acts as an <u>electrical insulator</u>, <u>speeding up</u> the impulse.

4) Neurones are <u>long</u>, which also <u>speeds up</u> the impulse (<u>connecting</u> with <u>another neurone</u> slows the impulse down, so one long neurone is much <u>quicker</u> than lots of short ones joined together).

A typical neurone

Cell body | Nucleus | Insulating sheath

Dentrites | Axon

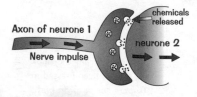

Axon of neurone 1

Nerve impulse

chemicals released

neurone 2

5) The <u>connection</u> between <u>two neurones</u> is a very tiny gap called a <u>synapse</u>:

- The electrical impulse triggers the release of <u>transmitter chemicals</u>, which <u>diffuse</u> across the gap.
- These chemicals bind to <u>receptor molecules</u> in the membrane of the <u>next neurone</u>. This sets off a <u>new electrical impulse</u>.

Reflex Actions Stop You Injuring Yourself

1) <u>Reflex actions</u> are <u>involuntary</u> (done without thinking) so they're <u>even quicker</u> than normal responses. The passage of information in a reflex (from receptor to effector) is called a <u>reflex arc</u>.

2) The <u>conscious brain</u> isn't involved in a <u>reflex arc</u>. The <u>sensory neurone</u> connects to a <u>relay neurone</u> in the <u>spinal cord</u> or in an <u>unconscious part of the brain</u> — which links <u>directly</u> to the <u>right motor neurone</u>, so no time's <u>wasted</u> thinking about the response.

3) Reflex actions often have a <u>protective role</u>, e.g. snatching back your hand when you touch a <u>burning hot</u> plate.

Relay neurones just connect sensory neurones to motor neurones.

The conscious brain can sometimes override a reflex response, e.g. to stop us dropping a hot plate we don't want to break. This involves a neurone that connects to the motor neurone in the reflex arc.

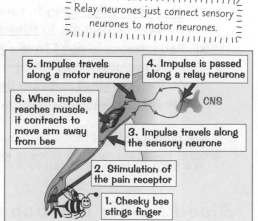

5. Impulse travels along a motor neurone

4. Impulse is passed along a relay neurone

6. When impulse reaches muscle, it contracts to move arm away from bee

CNS

3. Impulse travels along the sensory neurone

2. Stimulation of the pain receptor

1. Cheeky bee stings finger

Don't let the thought of exams play on your nerves...

Reflexes allow organisms to respond rapidly to a stimulus — they're often essential for survival.

Q1   Name the two main parts of the central nervous system.   [2 marks]

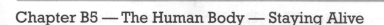

The Brain

Scientists know a bit about the <u>brain</u> but <u>not as much</u> as they'd like. <u>Research</u> into the brain has the potential to <u>change lives</u> — especially because our life expectancy is increasing, but our <u>brain function declines with age</u>.

The Brain is Responsible for Complex Behaviours

The brain is made up of <u>billions</u> of <u>interconnected neurones</u> (neurones that are connected together). It <u>controls</u> and <u>coordinates</u> everything you do — running, breathing, sleeping, remembering your gym kit. We know that <u>different regions</u> of the brain carry out <u>different functions</u>:

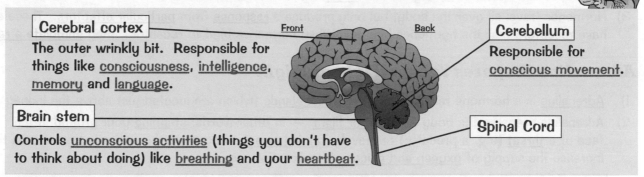

Cerebral cortex
The outer wrinkly bit. Responsible for things like <u>consciousness</u>, <u>intelligence</u>, <u>memory</u> and <u>language</u>.

Front   Back

Cerebellum
Responsible for <u>conscious movement</u>.

Brain stem
Controls <u>unconscious activities</u> (things you don't have to think about doing) like <u>breathing</u> and your <u>heartbeat</u>.

Spinal Cord

Scientists Use a Range of Methods to Study the Brain

A <u>single area</u> of our brain can perform <u>many different functions</u> — scientists use a few different methods to study the brain and figure out <u>which bits do what</u>:

Scientists that study the brain are called neuroscientists.

1) <u>Studying patients with brain damage</u> — If a <u>small</u> part of the brain has been <u>damaged</u>, the <u>effect</u> this has on the patient can tell you a lot about what the damaged part of the brain does. E.g. if an area at the back of the brain was damaged by a stroke and the patient went <u>blind</u>, you know that that area has something to do with <u>vision</u>. However, if a person is <u>severely brain damaged</u>, it may be <u>unethical</u> to study them as they might not be able to give <u>informed consent</u>.

2) <u>Electrically stimulating the brain</u> — The brain can be <u>stimulated electrically</u> by pushing a tiny <u>electrode</u> into the tissue and giving it a small zap of electricity. By observing what stimulating <u>different parts</u> of the brain does, it's possible to get an idea of what those parts do. E.g. when a certain part of the brain (known as the <u>motor area</u>) is stimulated, it causes <u>muscle contraction</u> and <u>movement</u>.

3) <u>fMRI scans</u> — Functional magnetic resonance imaging (fMRI) scanners are big fancy tube-like machines that can be used to show which parts of the brain are <u>activated</u> when performing certain tasks <u>inside the scanner</u> (like listening to music or trying to recall a memory).

Even with all this technology, our <u>knowledge of brain functions</u> and our <u>ability to investigate</u> them is still <u>limited</u>. That's because the brain is <u>complex</u>, it's <u>hard to access</u> certain areas, and <u>test results</u> can be <u>hard</u> to <u>interpret</u>.

Treating Problems in the Brain Can be Tricky

Many things can <u>go wrong</u> with the <u>brain</u> or other parts of the nervous system, e.g. <u>injuries</u> to the brain or <u>spinal cord</u>, <u>tumours</u>, <u>diseases</u>, etc. These can be <u>difficult</u> to treat successfully:

- If a problem occurs in a part of the nervous system that's <u>not easy to access</u> it can be hard to treat, e.g. it's not possible to <u>surgically remove</u> tumours growing in certain parts of the brain.

- Treatment for problems in the nervous system may lead to <u>permanent damage</u>, e.g. surgery to remove a brain tumour may leave <u>surrounding parts</u> of the brain permanently damaged.

- It's <u>hard to repair damage</u> to the nervous system. <u>Neurones</u> don't readily <u>repair themselves</u> because, once they've differentiated, they <u>don't undergo mitosis</u> (see p.59). This means they <u>can't divide</u> to <u>replace</u> lost neurones. Scientists are investigating the use of <u>stem cells</u> to replace damaged tissue in the nervous system — but there are <u>ethical issues</u> surrounding stem cell use (see p.63).

A whole page dedicated to that squidgy thing in your head...

...lucky you. But actually it's really fascinating stuff. It'll make it that bit easier to learn...

Q1   Name the region of the brain that controls conscious movement.   [1 mark]

Hormones and Negative Feedback

The other way to <u>send information</u> around the body (apart from along neurones) is by using <u>hormones</u>.

Hormones are *Chemical Messengers* Sent in the Blood

1) Hormones are chemicals produced in various <u>glands</u> called <u>endocrine glands</u>. These glands make up your <u>endocrine system</u>. Like the nervous system, the endocrine system allows you to respond to both <u>internal</u> and <u>external stimuli</u>.

2) Hormones are released directly into the <u>blood</u>. The blood then carries them to other parts of the body.

3) Hormones travel all over the body, but only produce a <u>response</u> from <u>particular effectors</u>. These effectors have <u>receptors</u> that the hormones <u>bind to</u>. When hormones bind to receptors, they <u>stimulate a response</u>.

Hormones are slow compared to nervous impulses but they have longer-lasting effects.

Adrenaline Prepares You for 'Fight or Flight'

1) <u>Adrenaline</u> is a hormone released by the <u>adrenal glands</u> (which are located just above the kidneys).

2) Adrenaline prepares the body for '<u>fight or flight</u>' — in other words, <u>standing</u> your <u>ground</u> in the face of a <u>threat</u> (e.g. a predator) or bravely <u>running away</u>. It does this by activating processes that increase the supply of <u>oxygen and glucose</u> to cells. For example:

> • Adrenaline <u>binds</u> to specific <u>receptors</u> in the <u>heart</u>. This causes the heart muscle (the <u>effector</u>) to <u>contract</u> more frequently and with <u>more force</u>, so heart rate and blood pressure <u>increase</u>.
>
> • This increases <u>blood flow</u> to the <u>muscles</u>, so the cells receive more <u>oxygen</u> and <u>glucose</u> for increased <u>respiration</u>.
>
> • Adrenaline also binds to receptors in the <u>liver</u>. This causes the liver to <u>break down</u> its <u>glycogen</u> stores (see p.82) to release <u>glucose</u>.
>
> • This increases the <u>blood glucose level</u>, so there's more glucose in the blood to be transported to the cells.

3) When your brain detects a <u>stressful situation</u>, it sends <u>nervous impulses</u> to the <u>adrenal glands</u>, which respond by secreting <u>adrenaline</u>. This gets the body ready for <u>action</u>.

Hormone Release can be Affected by Negative Feedback

Your body can <u>control</u> the levels of hormones (and other substances) in the blood using <u>negative feedback systems</u>. When the body detects that the level of a substance has gone <u>above or below</u> the <u>normal level</u>, it <u>triggers a response</u> to bring the level <u>back to normal</u> again. Here's an example of just that:

Thyroxine Regulates Metabolism

1) <u>Thyroxine</u> is a hormone released by the <u>thyroid gland</u> (found in the <u>neck</u>).

2) It plays an important role in regulating <u>metabolic rate</u> — the speed at which chemical reactions in the body occur. It's important for loads of processes in the body, such as <u>growth</u> and <u>protein synthesis</u>.

3) Thyroxine is released in response to <u>thyroid stimulating hormone</u> (<u>TSH</u>), which is released from the <u>pituitary gland</u>.

4) A <u>negative feedback system</u> keeps the amount of thyroxine in the blood at the right level — when the level of thyroxine in the blood is <u>higher than normal</u>, the secretion of <u>TSH</u> from the pituitary gland is <u>inhibited</u>. This reduces the amount of thyroxine released from the thyroid gland so the level in the blood <u>falls</u> back towards normal.

Thyroxine is made in the thyroid gland from iodine and amino acids.

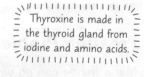

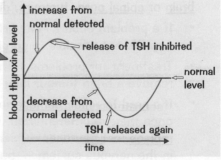

blood thyroxine level — increase from normal detected — release of TSH inhibited — normal level — decrease from normal detected — TSH released again — time

---

Negative feedback sucks, especially from your science teacher...

Hormones and negative feedback both crop up again in this book — best learn this page good 'n' proper.

Q1   Explain how the endocrine system allows communication within the body.   [5 marks]

Hormones in Reproduction

You need to know about <u>sex hormones</u> and how some of them <u>interact</u> to control the <u>menstrual cycle</u>.

Hormones are Needed for Sexual Reproduction

Human <u>sexual reproduction</u> would be <u>impossible without hormones</u>. Hormones regulate the female <u>menstrual cycle</u> — this is the <u>monthly sequence of events</u> in which the female body releases an <u>egg</u> (ovulation) and prepares the <u>uterus</u> (womb) in case the egg is <u>fertilised</u>. The cycle has <u>four stages</u>:

<u>Stage 1</u> <u>Day 1 is when menstruation starts.</u>
The lining of the uterus breaks down and is released.

> The fancy name for the lining of the uterus is the 'endometrium'.

<u>Stage 2</u> <u>The uterus lining is repaired</u>, from day 4 to day 14, until it becomes a thick spongy layer full of blood vessels ready for a fertilised egg to implant there.

<u>Stage 3</u> <u>An egg develops and is released</u> from the ovary (<u>ovulation</u>) at about day 14.

<u>Stage 4</u> <u>The lining is then maintained</u> for about 14 days, until day 28. If no fertilised egg has landed on the uterus wall by day 28, the spongy lining starts to break down again and the whole cycle starts over.

Stage 1 | Stage 2 | Stage 3 | Stage 4 | Next Cycle

Lining of uterus breaks down | Lining of the uterus builds up | Egg released | Lining of uterus maintained

Day 1 | Day 4 | Day 14 | Day 28 | Day 4

The Menstrual Cycle is Controlled by Four Hormones

❶ FSH (follicle-stimulating hormone)

1) Released by the <u>pituitary gland</u>.
2) Causes a <u>follicle</u> (an <u>egg</u> and its surrounding cells) to <u>mature</u> in one of the ovaries.
3) Stimulates <u>oestrogen</u> production.

❷ Oestrogen

1) Released by the <u>ovaries</u>.
2) Causes the lining of the uterus to <u>thicken</u> and <u>grow</u>.

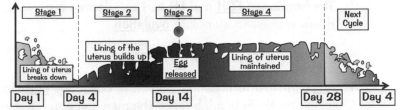

follicle matures | ovulation | corpus luteum

FSH | LH | Oestrogen | Progesterone

Lining of uterus breaks down | Lining of the uterus builds up | Lining of the uterus maintained

Day 1 | Day 4 | Day 14 | Day 28

❸ LH (luteinising hormone)

1) Released by the <u>pituitary gland</u>.
2) An LH <u>surge</u> (rapid increase) stimulates <u>ovulation</u> at day 14 — the follicle ruptures and the <u>egg is released</u>.
3) Stimulates the <u>remains</u> of the <u>follicle</u> to develop into a structure called a <u>corpus luteum</u> — which secretes <u>progesterone</u>.

❹ Progesterone

1) Released by the <u>ovaries</u>.
2) <u>Maintains</u> the lining of the uterus for the <u>implantation</u> of a fertilised egg.
3) Along with <u>oestrogen</u>, progesterone <u>inhibits</u> the release of <u>FSH</u> and <u>LH</u>.
4) When the level of progesterone <u>falls</u>, and there's a low oestrogen level, the uterus lining <u>breaks down</u>.
5) A <u>low</u> progesterone level allows <u>FSH</u> to <u>increase</u> (and then the whole cycle starts again).

If a fertilised egg implants in the uterus (i.e. the woman becomes <u>pregnant</u>) then the level of <u>progesterone</u> will <u>stay high</u> to maintain the lining of the uterus during pregnancy.

What do you call a fish with no eye — FSH...

OK, this stuff is pretty tricky. Try scribbling down everything on the page until you can get it all without peeking.

Q1   Explain the role of LH in the menstrual cycle.   [2 marks]

Hormones for Fertility and Contraception

Hormones play a big role in <u>reproduction</u>. No surprise then that hormones are used to help <u>infertile</u> women <u>have babies</u> and to help <u>fertile</u> women <u>not have babies</u>. What a topsy-turvy world we live in.

Hormones can be Used to Treat Infertility

If a person is <u>infertile</u>, it means they <u>can't reproduce naturally</u>. Infertility can now be <u>treated</u> due to developments in <u>modern reproductive technologies</u>, many of which involve <u>hormones</u>.

Hormones are Used to Promote Natural Pregnancy...

1) Some women have levels of <u>FSH</u> (see previous page) that are <u>too low</u> to cause the follicle to develop and their <u>eggs to mature</u>. This means that <u>no ovulation</u> takes place (<u>no eggs</u> are <u>released</u>) and the women <u>can't get pregnant</u>.

2) The hormones <u>FSH</u> and <u>LH</u> can be injected by these women to stimulate <u>ovulation</u>.

> *The use of hormones to treat infertility has helped many people — it's a good example of a positive application of scientific technology.*

...and They Play a Role in IVF

1) <u>IVF</u> ("*in vitro* fertilisation") involves collecting <u>eggs</u> from the woman's ovaries and fertilising them in a <u>lab</u> using the man's <u>sperm</u>. These are then grown into <u>embryos</u>.

2) Once the embryos are <u>tiny balls of cells</u>, one or two of them are <u>transferred</u> to the woman's uterus to improve the chance of <u>pregnancy</u>.

3) <u>FSH</u> and <u>LH</u> are given before egg collection to <u>stimulate egg production</u> and <u>ovulation</u> so more than one egg can be collected (improving the chance of successful fertilisation).

> *See the next page for contraceptive methods that don't involve hormones.*

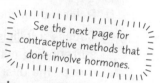

Hormones can be Used as Contraceptives

Contraceptives are used to <u>prevent pregnancy</u>. Some contraceptive methods involve <u>hormones</u>:

Contraceptive method	Hormone(s) involved	How it works
<u>Injection</u> — effective for up to 3 months.	Progesterone	• Stimulates the production of <u>thick cervical mucus</u> (at the entrance to the uterus) making it less likely that any sperm will get through and reach an egg. • <u>Thins the lining of the uterus</u> to reduce the chance of a fertilised egg <u>implanting</u>. • <u>Prevents ovulation</u>* by inhibiting the production of <u>FSH</u> and <u>LH</u> (see previous page). *not true for all types of mini-pill
<u>Implant</u> — inserted beneath the skin of the arm. Effective for 3 years.		
<u>Intrauterine system (IUS)</u> — a T-shaped piece of plastic inserted into the uterus. Effective for 3-5 years.		
<u>Mini-pill</u> (aka progesterone-only pill) — has to be taken every day.		
<u>Combined pill</u> — taken in a '21 day pill, 7 days no pill' cycle.	Progesterone and oestrogen	All of the effects of progesterone listed above, plus oestrogen also <u>prevents ovulation</u> by inhibiting FSH. *The mini-pill and the combined pill are 'oral contraceptives'.*
<u>Patch</u> — worn on the skin in a 4-week cycle (replaced once a week for 3 weeks, then no patch worn for a week).		

If <u>used correctly</u> (e.g. pills taken on time) all of these contraceptive methods are <u>more than 99% effective</u>.

IVF... FSH... IUS... LH... — I feel like I'm at the opticians...

Hormones can be used to manipulate the menstrual cycle so that the reproductive system does what we want it to do, when we want it to do it. Great for both increasing and decreasing the chance of pregnancy.

Q1   Explain how hormones may be used to promote a natural pregnancy in an infertile woman.   **[3 marks]**

More on Contraception

There are ways to prevent pregnancy that <u>don't</u> include the use of hormones. Now, as a warning, this page does include themes of a <u>sexual nature</u> from the outset. You might not want to read it aloud to your parents.

There are Plenty of Non-Hormonal Contraceptive Methods

1) <u>Barrier methods</u> — these try to stop the egg and sperm meeting. For example:

> - <u>Condom</u> (<u>98% effective</u>) — worn over the <u>penis</u> during intercourse to prevent sperm entering the vagina.
> - <u>Female condom</u> (<u>95% effective</u>) — worn inside the <u>vagina</u> during intercourse.
> - <u>Diaphragm</u> (<u>92-96% effective</u>) — fits over the <u>cervix</u> (opening of the uterus) to stop sperm from meeting the egg. Has to be fitted by a GP/nurse the first time it's used and has to be used with a <u>spermicide</u> (a chemical that kills sperm).

The figures given here for effectiveness assume that the methods are used properly.

2) <u>Intrauterine devices</u> (<u>IUDs</u>) — T-shaped devices that contain <u>copper</u>. They're <u>inserted</u> into the <u>uterus</u> and prevent sperm from surviving. They also alter the lining of the womb so that fertilised eggs can't implant. They're more than <u>99% effective</u> and can be kept in for up to <u>ten years</u>.

3) <u>'Natural' methods</u> — these don't use any bits and bobs like all the other methods. They refer to basically just <u>not having sexual intercourse</u> when the woman is <u>most fertile</u> (the period around ovulation) or <u>'withdrawal'</u> (the man pulling the penis out before ejaculation). These methods are the <u>least effective</u> at preventing pregnancy as they rely on getting the timing exactly right.

4) <u>Sterilisation</u> — involves a <u>surgical procedure</u> to cut or tie tubes in the reproductive system. In women, the procedure means eggs are prevented from travelling from the ovaries to the uterus. In men, it prevents sperm from being ejaculated. The methods are <u>over 99% effective</u>.

There are Pros and Cons to All Forms of Contraception

In the exam you may have to <u>evaluate hormonal</u> (see previous page) and <u>non-hormonal</u> methods of contraception. Here are some things to think about:

1) <u>Side-effects</u> — <u>hormonal methods</u> can have unpleasant side-effects, e.g. heavy or irregular periods, acne, headaches, mood changes.

2) <u>Possibility of 'doing it wrong'</u> — <u>barrier methods</u> and <u>'natural' methods</u> have to be done <u>properly</u> each time a couple have intercourse. If, for example, a condom splits or a man doesn't withdraw soon enough, then the methods <u>won't work</u>. The same is true with some <u>hormonal</u> methods, e.g. if a woman doesn't take her pills correctly or replace her patch at the right time, the methods won't work properly.

I've got this barrier thing sorted...

3) <u>Medical input</u> — many methods involve at least one trip to a <u>nurse</u> or <u>doctor</u> (e.g. to get a prescription for pills or to have a device inserted). Although these methods tend to be more effective than barrier or 'natural' methods, people may feel <u>uncomfortable</u> about the procedures involved.

4) <u>Length of action</u> — <u>long-lasting methods</u> (i.e. those that last several months or years) may be <u>preferable</u> over having to think about contraception every day or every time intercourse is on the cards.

5) <u>Sexually transmitted infections</u> (<u>STIs</u>) — these are infections that are passed from person to person during sexual intercourse. The <u>only method</u> of contraception that can protect against them is <u>condoms</u> (male or female types).

The winner of best contraceptive ever — just not doing it...

By now you should be pretty clued up on the different methods of contraception. Whether hormonal or non-hormonal, no method is guaranteed to be 100% effective and each method has its own pros and cons.

Q1   Give one reason why a woman may prefer to use a diaphragm rather than an oral contraceptive.   [1 mark]

Q2   Give two advantages of using an intrauterine device (IUD) as a contraceptive method rather than male condoms.
            [2 marks]

Homeostasis

Homeostasis involves balancing body functions to maintain a 'constant internal environment'. Smashing.

Homeostasis is Maintaining a Constant Internal Environment

1) Conditions in your body need to be kept within a narrow range — this is really important so that all the enzyme-controlled metabolic reactions that take place in your cells continue at an appropriate rate. It can be dangerous for your health if conditions vary too much from normal levels.

2) To maintain a constant internal environment, your body needs to respond to both internal and external changes whilst balancing inputs (stuff going into your body) with outputs (stuff leaving).

3) It does this using receptors, nerves, hormones and effectors (muscles and glands). Some effectors involved in homeostasis are antagonistic — this means they work in opposition to one another (e.g. one increases a level and another decreases it).

4) Things that you need to keep steady include:

   • Blood glucose (sugar) concentration — you need to make sure the amount of glucose in your blood doesn't get too high or too low (see page 82).

   • Water content — you need to keep a balance between the water you gain (in drink, food and from respiration) and the water you urinate, sweat and breathe out. See pages 80-81 for more.

   • Body temperature — you need to make sure it doesn't get too high or too low (see below).

Body Temperature is Controlled by the Hypothalamus

All enzymes work best at a certain temperature. The enzymes in the human body work best at about 37 °C. The hypothalamus in your brain acts as your own personal thermostat. It contains receptors that are sensitive to the blood temperature in the brain. It also receives impulses from receptors in the skin (nerve endings) that provide information about the external temperature. When the hypothalamus detects a change, it causes a response in the dermis (deep layer of the skin):

See p.32 for more on enzymes.

When you're too hot:

1) Erector muscles relax, so hairs lie flat.

2) Lots of sweat (containing water and salts) is produced. When the sweat evaporates, it transfers energy from your skin to the environment, cooling you down.

3) Muscles in the walls of blood vessels close to the surface of the skin relax. This causes the blood vessels to dilate (widen) and is called vasodilation. It allows more blood to flow near the surface, so it can transfer more energy into the surroundings, which cools you down.

temperature receptors (nerve endings)
sweat gland
hair erector muscle
blood vessels dilate

When you're too cold:

1) Erector muscles contract. Hairs stand on end to trap an insulating layer of air, which helps keep you warm.

2) Very little sweat is produced.

3) Muscles in the walls of blood vessels near the surface of the skin contract. This causes the vessels to constrict (narrow) and is called vasoconstriction. It means less blood flows near the surface, so less energy is transferred to the surroundings.

4) When you're cold you shiver too (your muscles contract automatically). This needs respiration, which transfers some energy to warm the body.

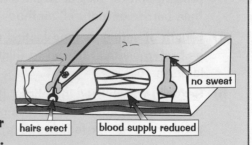

no sweat
hairs erect
blood supply reduced

Learn about homeostasis — and keep your cool...

Make sure you learn the definition of homeostasis and can explain how your body responds to temperature changes.

Q1   Explain how blood flow through the skin is affected when a person is too cold.   [3 marks]

More on Homeostasis

The key to understanding homeostasis is to get your head around <u>negative feedback</u>...

There's more on negative feedback on page 74.

Homeostatic Systems Respond by Negative Feedback

The control of <u>body temperature</u> (described on the previous page) involves negative feedback:

1) <u>Receptors</u> in the skin and hypothalamus detect when the temperature is <u>too high</u> or <u>too low</u>.

2) The <u>hypothalamus</u> then <u>processes</u> the information and communicates via the <u>nervous system</u> with <u>effectors</u>, e.g. erector muscles in the skin or sweat glands.

3) The effectors <u>respond</u> to <u>counteract</u> the change — bringing the temperature <u>back</u> to <u>normal</u>.

4) Negative feedback helps to keep conditions in the body <u>within certain limits</u> — it usually <u>keeps</u> body temperature <u>within 0.5 °C</u> above or below <u>37 °C</u>.

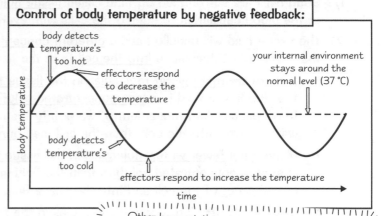

Control of body temperature by negative feedback:

body detects temperature's too hot

effectors respond to decrease the temperature

your internal environment stays around the normal level (37 °C)

body detects temperature's too cold

effectors respond to increase the temperature

body temperature

time

Other homeostatic systems are also controlled by negative feedback, and can involve communication via hormones rather than the nervous system, e.g. controlling water content (p.80-81) and blood sugar level (p.82).

You can Model Temperature Control in the Body | PRACTICAL

For example, you could investigate how negative feedback works by attempting to <u>control the temperature</u> of a <u>beaker of water</u>. You can model how a <u>single effector</u> (a Bunsen burner) controls temperature:

1) Place a <u>Bunsen burner</u> on a <u>heat-proof mat</u>, and a <u>tripod</u> and <u>gauze</u> over the Bunsen burner. Put a <u>beaker of water</u> on top of the tripod.

2) Use a <u>thermometer</u> to <u>measure</u> the <u>temperature of the water</u>. Then use the <u>Bunsen burner</u> to carefully heat the water to <u>40 °C</u>.

3) When the temperature of the water <u>gets above 40 °C</u>, <u>turn off</u> the Bunsen burner — this models the body detecting that the temperature is <u>too high</u>, and an <u>effector</u> responding in an attempt to <u>lower the temperature</u>.

4) Use a <u>stopwatch</u> to <u>record how long</u> it takes for the <u>water to return to 40 °C</u>.

5) When the temperature of the water <u>falls below 40 °C</u>, relight the Bunsen burner — this models the body detecting that the temperature is <u>too low</u>, and an <u>effector</u> responding in an attempt to <u>increase the temperature</u>.

6) Try to keep the water at 40 °C by <u>monitoring</u> the temperature and <u>responding</u> to the changes.

You can also use a similar model to investigate whether two <u>antagonistic effectors</u> (two effectors working in opposition, see previous page) are <u>more or less effective</u> than a single effector:

1) Carry out steps 1 and 2 from the method above.

2) When the temperature of the water gets above 40 °C, <u>turn off</u> the Bunsen burner and carefully add an <u>ice cube</u> to the water (you may need more than one). Give it a bit of a <u>stir</u>. By adding the ice cube, you're modelling an <u>antagonistic effector</u> — the <u>cooling effect</u> of the <u>ice cube</u> works in opposition to the <u>heating effect</u> of the <u>Bunsen burner</u>.

3) Use a <u>stopwatch</u> to <u>record how long</u> it takes for the <u>water to return to 40 °C</u>.

4) <u>Compare</u> these results with those of a single effector (just the Bunsen burner). Was it <u>easier</u> to control the temperature with <u>just</u> the Bunsen burner or <u>both</u> the ice and the Bunsen burner?

Television has an antagonistic effect on my motivation to revise...

I'm detecting that you need a rest. Take a quick break, grab a biscuit and let your mind return to a normal level.

Q1 Describe how negative feedback is used to control body temperature. [3 marks]

Controlling Water Content

The <u>kidneys</u> are really important in this whole homeostasis thing — they help regulate <u>water content</u>.

Balancing Water Content is Really Important

1) Body cells are surrounded by fluid called <u>tissue fluid</u>. It's squeezed out of the <u>blood capillaries</u> to supply the cells with everything they need.

Look back at page 37 for a reminder of osmosis.

2) The tissue fluid will usually have a <u>different concentration</u> to the fluid <u>inside</u> a cell. This means that water will either move <u>into the cell</u> from the tissue fluid, or <u>out of the cell</u>, by <u>osmosis</u>:

• If there are <u>more water molecules</u> in the <u>tissue fluid</u> than in the cell (i.e. the tissue fluid is a <u>less concentrated solution</u> than the fluid in the cell), there will be a net movement of water <u>into</u> the cell by osmosis. If too much water moves into the cell, then the cell may <u>burst</u> — this is called <u>lysis</u>.

• If there are <u>fewer water molecules</u> in the <u>tissue fluid</u> than in the cell (i.e. the tissue fluid is a <u>more concentrated solution</u> than the fluid in the cell), there will be a net movement of water <u>out of</u> the cell and into the tissue fluid. This causes the cell to <u>shrink</u>.

• If the concentration of water molecules in the tissue fluid and the cell are <u>roughly the same</u>, the cell will <u>stay the same</u>.

Animal cells burst when they contain too much water because they don't have a rigid cell wall (unlike plant cells).

3) So it's really important that the <u>water content</u> of the <u>blood</u> (and therefore of the tissue fluid) is <u>controlled</u> to keep cells functioning normally.

Kidneys Help Balance Water Content

1) The kidneys play a vital role in <u>balancing the level</u> of <u>water</u> in the body — they control how much water is <u>lost in urine</u> by varying the <u>volume</u> of urine produced and how <u>concentrated</u> it is.

2) The kidneys also get rid of <u>waste</u> and control the levels of <u>other substances</u> in the body.

3) They have millions of little structures inside them called <u>kidney tubules</u>.

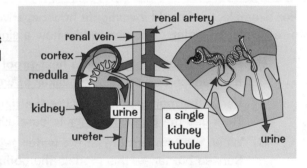

renal artery
renal vein
cortex
medulla
kidney
urine
ureter
a single kidney tubule
urine

Urine is Formed in the Tubules

This is what happens...

Blood flows through the <u>glomerulus</u> at <u>high pressure</u> and small molecules including <u>water</u>, <u>sugar</u>, <u>salt</u> (sodium chloride) and <u>urea</u> are filtered out into the <u>capsule</u>. The liquid then flows along the tubule and useful substances are <u>selectively reabsorbed</u>:

• <u>All</u> the <u>sugar</u> is reabsorbed.

• <u>Sufficient salt</u> is reabsorbed. Excess salt isn't.

• <u>Sufficient water</u> is reabsorbed, according to the level of the hormone <u>ADH</u> (see next page). This helps to keep the <u>blood plasma</u> at the <u>correct concentration</u> to prevent cell lysis or shrinkage.

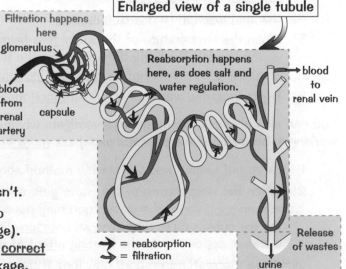

Enlarged view of a single tubule

Filtration happens here
glomerulus
blood from renal artery
capsule
Reabsorption happens here, as does salt and water regulation.
blood to renal vein
Release of wastes
urine
↗ = reabsorption
→ = filtration

Whatever isn't reabsorbed forms <u>urine</u>, which is excreted by the kidneys and stored in the <u>bladder</u>.

Reabsorb the facts and excrete the rest...

The kidneys are really important for making sure you have the right amount of water in your body. But they can't take all the credit — the brain is involved in the process too (as you'll find out on the next page).

Q1   Explain what might happen to an animal cell surrounded by a less concentrated solution.   [2 marks]

More on Controlling Water Content

Think you know all you need to know about <u>urine production</u>? Well you don't. Here's another page about <u>wee</u>.

The Concentration of Urine is Controlled by a Hormone

1) The concentration of urine is controlled by a hormone called <u>anti-diuretic hormone</u> (<u>ADH</u>). This is released into the <u>bloodstream</u> by the <u>pituitary gland</u>.

2) The <u>hypothalamus</u> contains <u>receptors</u> that are sensitive to <u>the water content of the blood</u>. The hypothalamus processes the information it receives from these receptors and instructs the <u>pituitary gland</u> to release <u>ADH</u> into the blood according to how much is needed.

3) ADH makes the <u>kidney tubules more permeable</u> so that more water is reabsorbed back into the blood.

4) The whole process of water content regulation is controlled by <u>negative feedback</u> (see page 74). This means that if the water content gets <u>too high</u> or <u>too low</u>, a mechanism will be triggered that brings it back to <u>normal</u>.

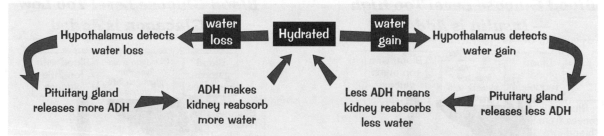

5) So, using negative feedback, the amount of water in your body can be closely regulated. The <u>more water</u> your kidneys reabsorb, the <u>less water</u> will pass out as <u>urine</u> — so you'll produce a <u>smaller volume</u> of urine. Your kidneys will still excrete all the <u>waste products</u> they need to though, so your urine will be more <u>concentrated</u> (as it contains the same amount of waste substances but less water).

Your Urine isn't Always the Same

As you've seen, the <u>volume</u> and <u>concentration</u> of urine depends on the <u>water content of the blood</u>. This can vary with <u>osmotic challenges</u>, such as...

<u>Sweating and dehydration</u> — losing more water than you take in causes <u>dehydration</u>. This can happen when it's <u>hot</u> or when you exercise (which makes you hot) because you <u>sweat more</u>. Sweat contains water, so sweating causes <u>water loss</u>.

- <u>Water loss</u> is detected by <u>receptors</u> in the hypothalamus.
- The <u>hypothalamus</u> processes this change and instructs the <u>pituitary gland</u> to release <u>more ADH</u>.
- This makes the <u>kidneys reabsorb more water</u>, so the water content of the blood <u>increases</u> and only a <u>small volume</u> of <u>concentrated</u> urine is produced.

The <u>brain</u> also triggers feelings of <u>thirst</u> when you're dehydrated. This makes you want to <u>drink more</u>, which helps to <u>restore water balance</u> in the body.

I'm sweaty and I know it...

<u>Excess water intake</u> — receptors in the hypothalamus detect an <u>increase</u> in blood <u>water content</u> and the pituitary gland secretes <u>less ADH</u>. The kidneys <u>reabsorb less water</u>, so <u>lots</u> of <u>dilute</u> urine will be produced — this <u>lowers</u> the blood water content.

Learn this lot or else urine trouble come exam time...

Make sure you understand how the brain and kidneys work together to control urine production and how this in turn helps to control water content in the body. Then you can do a little dance to celebrate water content regulation.

Q1   Describe the role of ADH in the body.   [3 marks]

Q2   Explain why a person may feel more thirsty than normal on a hot day.   [3 marks]

Controlling Blood Sugar Level

Blood sugar level is controlled as part of homeostasis. Insulin and glucagon are the two hormones involved.

Insulin and Glucagon Control Blood Sugar Level

1) Eating foods containing carbohydrate puts glucose into the blood from the small intestine.
2) The normal metabolism of cells removes glucose from the blood.
3) Vigorous exercise removes much more glucose from the blood.
4) Excess glucose can be stored as glycogen in the liver and in the muscles.
5) When these stores are full then the excess glucose is stored as lipid (fat) in the tissues.
6) The level of glucose in the blood must be kept steady. Changes in blood glucose are monitored and controlled by the pancreas, using the hormones insulin and glucagon. These hormones work antagonistically — they have opposite effects to return the body to normal conditions:

Blood Glucose Level Too High — Insulin is Added

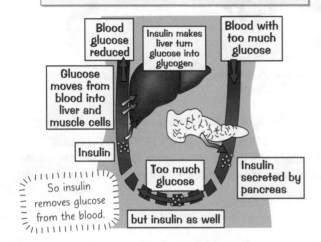

Blood Glucose Level Too Low — Glucagon is Added

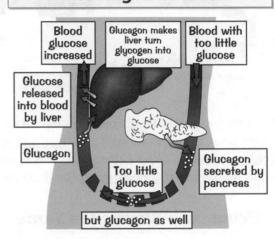

Having Diabetes Means You Can't Control Your Blood Sugar Level

Diabetes is a condition that affects your ability to control your blood sugar level. There are two types:

TYPE 1

Type 1 diabetes is where the pancreas stops producing insulin. The result is that a person's blood glucose level can rise to a level that can kill them. People with type 1 diabetes need insulin therapy. This usually involves injecting insulin into the blood several times a day (often at mealtimes). This makes sure that glucose is removed from the blood quickly once food has been digested. This stops the level of glucose in the blood from getting too high and is a very effective treatment. The amount of insulin needed depends on the person's diet and how active they are. As well as insulin therapy, people with type 1 diabetes need to think about limiting their intake of food rich in simple carbohydrates, e.g. sugars (which cause the blood glucose to rise rapidly) and taking regular exercise (which helps to remove excess glucose from the blood).

TYPE 2

Type 2 diabetes is where a person becomes resistant to insulin (their body's cells don't respond properly to the hormone) or the pancreas doesn't produce enough insulin. This can also cause blood sugar level to rise to a dangerous level. Being overweight can increase your chance of developing type 2 diabetes, as obesity is a major risk factor in the development of the disease (see page 24). Type 2 diabetes can be controlled by eating a healthy diet (this includes replacing simple carbohydrates with complex carbohydrates, e.g. wholegrains), exercising regularly and losing weight if necessary. Some people with type 2 diabetes also have medication or insulin injections.

And people used to think the pancreas was just a cushion...

This stuff can seem a bit confusing at first, but if you learn those two diagrams, it'll all start to get a lot easier.

Q1   Describe how the level of insulin production differs in type 1 and type 2 diabetes.   [3 marks]

The Eye

The <u>eye</u> is a <u>sense organ</u>. There are several parts you need to learn about, so get <u>focused</u>.

Learn the Eye with All Its Labels

The <u>tissues</u> in the eye are all <u>adapted</u> for their <u>functions</u>:

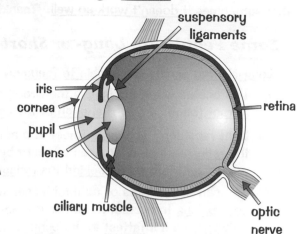

1) The CORNEA is the <u>transparent</u> outer layer found at the <u>front</u> of the eye. It <u>refracts</u> (bends) light into the eye.

2) The IRIS contains <u>muscles</u> that allow it to control the <u>diameter</u> of the PUPIL (the <u>hole</u> in the <u>middle</u>) and therefore <u>how much light</u> enters the eye.

3) The LENS also <u>refracts light</u>, <u>focusing</u> it onto the RETINA (which contains receptor cells sensitive to <u>light</u>).

4) The shape of the lens is controlled by the CILIARY MUSCLES and SUSPENSORY LIGAMENTS.

5) The OPTIC NERVE carries impulses from the receptors on the retina to the <u>brain</u>.

The Iris Reflex — Adjusting for Bright Light

There's more on reflexes on page 72.

<u>Very bright</u> light can <u>damage</u> the retina — so you have a reflex to protect it.

1) When <u>light receptors</u> in the eye detect very bright light, a <u>reflex</u> is triggered that makes the pupil <u>smaller</u>. The <u>circular muscles</u> in the iris <u>contract</u> and the <u>radial muscles relax</u>. This reduces the amount of light that can enter the eye.

2) The opposite process happens in dim light. This time, the <u>radial muscles contract</u> and the <u>circular muscles relax</u>, which makes the pupil <u>wider</u>.

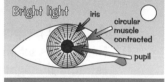

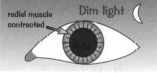

You can <u>investigate</u> these <u>reflex actions</u> by <u>dimming the lights</u> and timing how long it takes for your pupils (or a friend's) to <u>widen</u>. When you turn up the lights, you can see the pupils <u>return</u> to <u>normal</u> as the <u>circular muscles</u> in the iris <u>contract</u>.

Focusing on Near and Distant Objects — Another Reflex

The eye focuses light on the retina by <u>changing</u> the <u>shape</u> of the <u>lens</u> — this is known as <u>accommodation</u>.

To look at near objects:

1) The <u>ciliary muscles contract</u>, which <u>slackens</u> the <u>suspensory ligaments</u>.

2) The lens becomes <u>fat</u> (more curved).

3) This <u>increases</u> the amount by which it <u>refracts</u> light.

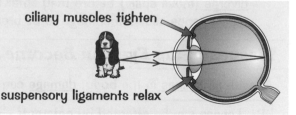

To look at distant objects:

1) The <u>ciliary muscles relax</u>, which allows the <u>suspensory ligaments</u> to <u>pull tight</u>.

2) This makes the lens go <u>thin</u> (less curved).

3) So it <u>refracts</u> light by a <u>smaller</u> amount.

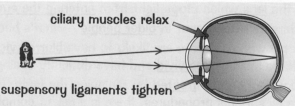

The diagrams here are called ray diagrams. They show the path taken by light rays as they enter the eye and are refracted onto the retina.

If the lens cannot refract the light by the <u>right amount</u> (so that it converges on the <u>retina</u>) the person will be <u>short-</u> or <u>long-sighted</u> — see the next page for more.

Eye eye, Captain...

It doesn't matter how good you are at blagging in the exam — you need to learn those diagrams of the eye.

Q1   Explain how the eye focuses on an object that's close to it.

[4 marks]

Correcting Vision Defects

As you can see on the previous page, the way the eye works is quite <u>complex</u>. It's not surprising really that sometimes it <u>doesn't work so well</u>. Thankfully, we have ways of <u>correcting</u> it...

Some People are Long- or Short-Sighted

<u>Long-sighted</u> people are <u>unable to focus</u> on <u>near</u> objects:

1) This occurs when the <u>lens</u> is the wrong shape and <u>doesn't</u> <u>refract</u> (bend) the light <u>enough</u> or the <u>eyeball</u> is too <u>short</u>.

2) Light rays <u>don't converge</u> (meet at a point) on the <u>retina</u> — instead images of near objects are brought into focus <u>behind</u> the <u>retina</u>.

3) You can use glasses or contact lenses with a <u>convex lens</u> to correct it. A convex lens <u>curves</u> <u>outwards</u> so it's <u>fattest</u> in the <u>centre</u>. The lens <u>refracts light</u> so it starts to <u>converge</u> before it enters the eye. The <u>increased convergence</u> allows the image to be brought into focus on the retina.

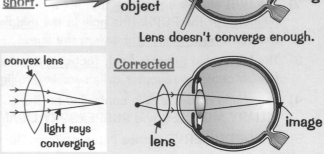

As you get older, your eye's lens loses flexibility, so it can't easily spring back into shape. This means light can't be focused well for near viewing — so older people are often long-sighted.

<u>Short-sighted</u> people are <u>unable to focus</u> on <u>distant</u> objects:

1) This occurs when the <u>lens</u> is the wrong shape and refracts the light <u>too much</u> or the <u>eyeball</u> is too <u>long</u>.

2) Light rays <u>converge</u> before they reach the <u>retina</u>, so images of distant objects are brought into focus <u>in front</u> of the <u>retina</u>.

3) You can use glasses or contact lenses with a <u>concave lens</u> to correct it. A concave lens <u>curves inwards</u>, so it's <u>thinner</u> in the <u>centre</u> than at the edge. The lens refracts light so that light rays <u>diverge</u> (move apart) before they enter the eye. The <u>reduction</u> in <u>convergence</u> allows the image to be brought into focus on the <u>retina</u>.

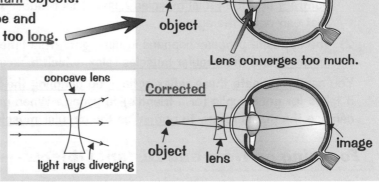

Tissues in the Eye can Become Damaged or Degrade

As with <u>all tissues</u> in the body, <u>damage</u> can occur to parts of the eye. For example:

1) <u>Lenses</u> can be affected by <u>cataracts</u>. A cataract is a <u>cloudy patch</u> on the <u>lens</u> which stops light from <u>entering the eye</u> normally.

2) Cataracts often occur in <u>older people</u> — that's because the <u>tissues</u> in the eye <u>degrade</u> over time.

3) People with cataracts are likely to have <u>blurred vision</u>. They may also experience colours looking <u>less vivid</u> and have difficulty seeing in <u>bright light</u>.

4) A cataract can be <u>treated</u> by replacing the faulty lens with an <u>artificial one</u> made of <u>clear plastic</u>. Like all surgical <u>procedures</u>, there is a risk of <u>complications</u>, including possible <u>damage</u> to the <u>retina</u> (which could lead to loss of sight).

If you can read this you've got better eyesight than me!

You might be asked to draw ray diagrams for different lenses in the exam, so make sure you totally understand what's going on in each of the ones shown above and on the previous page.

Q1   Give one way cataracts can be corrected. [1 mark]

Q2   Explain the cause of short-sightedness. [3 marks]

Revision Questions for Chapter B5

That was intense — luckily it's the end of Chapter B5.   Take a break, then test yourself with these questions.

• Try these questions and tick off each one when you get it right.

• When you've done all the questions for a topic and are completely happy with it, tick off the topic.

Exchange of Materials (p.67-68) ☑

1) Name three substances that humans have to exchange with their environment. ☑

2) How does having a large surface area to volume ratio help organisms exchange materials? ☑

3) Give an example of a specialised exchange surface found in a human and
explain how it is adapted to maximise the exchange of substances. ☑

The Circulatory System (p.69-71) ☑

4) Name the blood vessel that transports blood from the heart to the rest of the body. ☑

5) Describe the role of capillaries. ☑

6) Which type of blood vessel carries blood at high pressure? ☑

7) Name ten substances that are found in blood plasma. ☑

The Nervous System (p.72-73) ☑

8) Draw a diagram of a typical neurone and label all the parts. ☑

9) What is the purpose of a reflex action? ☑

10) Produce a sketch of the brain and label the cerebrum, cerebellum and brain stem. ☑

11) Give three reasons why it may be tricky to treat problems in the brain and other parts
of the nervous system. ☑

Hormones, The Menstrual Cycle and Controlling Fertility (p.74-77) ☑

12) What is a hormone? ☑

13) Describe how a negative feedback system works in the body. ☑

14) Draw a timeline of the 28 day menstrual cycle.
Label the four stages of the cycle and label when the egg is released. ☑

15) Describe how one non-hormonal method of contraception works and list its pros and cons. ☑

16) Briefly describe how IVF is carried out. ☑

Homeostasis (p.78-82) ☑

17) What is homeostasis? Why is it important?

18) What's an antagonistic effector? ☑

19) Explain how body temperature is reduced when you're too hot. ☑

20) Describe an experiment you could do to model temperature control in the body. ☑

21) Briefly describe how the kidneys produce urine. ☑

22) Name the hormone that controls the concentration of urine. ☑

23) What effect does the hormone glucagon have on blood glucose level? ☑

24) Explain how type 1 and type 2 diabetes can be treated. ☑

The Eye (p.83-84) ☑

25) Explain the roles of the following parts of the eye: a) cornea   b) iris   c) lens. ☑

26) Describe the iris reflex. Why is this needed? ☑

27) How is a convex lens used to correct long-sightedness? ☑

Natural Selection and Evolution

The <u>theory of evolution</u> states that one of your (probably very distant) ancestors was a <u>blob</u> in a swamp somewhere. Something like that, anyway. It's probably best to <u>read on</u> for more details...

Natural Selection Increases Advantageous Phenotypes

1) Populations of species usually show a lot of <u>genetic variation</u> — this means that there's a big <u>mix</u> of <u>genetic variants</u> (alleles) present in the population.

2) Genetic variants arise when DNA <u>randomly mutates</u> (changes).

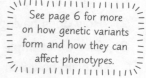

See page 6 for more on how genetic variants form and how they can affect phenotypes.

3) Occasionally, a genetic variant can have a <u>big</u> effect on an organism's <u>phenotype</u> (the characteristics it displays). However, most genetic variants have <u>no effect</u> on <u>phenotype</u> and <u>some</u> of them only have a <u>small influence</u> on a phenotype.

4) Those genetic variants that <u>do</u> affect phenotype can give rise to <u>characteristics</u> that make an organism <u>better suited</u> to a particular environment (e.g. being able to run away from predators faster). This means that the organisms that <u>inherit</u> these variants will have an <u>advantageous phenotype</u>.

5) The <u>resources</u> living things need to survive are <u>limited</u>. Individuals in a community must <u>compete</u> for these resources to <u>survive</u>. Individuals with genetic variants that give <u>advantageous phenotypes</u> will have a <u>better chance</u> of successfully <u>competing</u> for resources, and so have an increased chance of <u>surviving</u>, <u>reproducing</u> and passing on their <u>genes</u>.

6) This means that a <u>greater</u> proportion of individuals in the next generation will <u>inherit</u> the <u>advantageous variants</u> and so they'll also have the <u>phenotypes</u> that help <u>survival</u>.

7) Over many generations, the advantageous phenotype becomes <u>more common</u> in the population. The 'best' characteristics are <u>naturally selected</u> and the species becomes more and more <u>adapted</u> to its environment. Here's an example:

> Once upon a time maybe all rabbits had <u>short ears</u> and managed OK. Then one day a <u>mutated gene</u> meant that one rabbit popped out with <u>big ears</u>. This rabbit could hear better and was always the first to dive for cover at the sound of a predator. Pretty soon he's fathered a whole family of rabbits with <u>big ears</u>, all diving for cover before the other rabbits, and before you know it, there are only <u>big-eared</u> rabbits left — because the rest just didn't hear trouble coming quick enough.
>
> FOX!

Natural Selection Leads to the Evolution of Species

1) <u>Evolution</u> is the change in <u>inherited characteristics</u> of a population over <u>several generations</u>, through the process of <u>natural selection</u>.

2) Evolution by natural selection may mean that a species' <u>phenotype</u> changes so much that a completely <u>new species</u> is formed (i.e. the <u>old</u> and <u>new</u> version of the species wouldn't be able to <u>breed</u> together to produce <u>fertile offspring</u>). When a new species is formed it's called <u>speciation</u>.

3) Speciation can happen when a physical barrier <u>isolates two populations</u> of a species — conditions on each side of the barrier will be slightly <u>different</u> so the <u>phenotypes</u> that are <u>beneficial</u> will be <u>different</u> for each population. <u>Natural selection</u> acts on each population to increase the <u>proportion</u> of the <u>advantageous phenotype</u> in that population, until they are so <u>different</u> that they can no longer <u>breed together</u>.

4) The <u>speed</u> at which a species <u>evolves</u> depends partly on how quickly it <u>reproduces</u> — some species reproduce very <u>quickly</u> (e.g. <u>bacteria</u> can be ready to start dividing in just 20 minutes), whereas others reproduce much more <u>slowly</u> (e.g. usually <u>humans</u> only start reproducing after around 20-30 years).

'Natural selection' — sounds like vegan chocolates...

In terms of evolution, it's no good an organism being great at surviving if it doesn't breed and pass on its genes. And it'll only be good at surviving if it inherits great genetic variants or has awesome mutations in its DNA.

Q1   Musk oxen have thick fur, which is advantageous in the cold climate in which they live. Explain how the musk oxen may have developed this characteristic over many years.   [4 marks]

Evidence for Evolution

If you're sitting there thinking evolution is a load of <u>old codswallop</u>, here's a bit of <u>evidence</u> to help sway you...

There is Good Evidence for Evolution

Scientists believe that all <u>complex organisms</u> on Earth have evolved from <u>simple organisms</u> that existed about <u>3500 million years ago</u>. Of course, they wouldn't think this without good evidence to back it up. <u>Fossil records</u> and <u>antibiotic resistance in bacteria</u> both provide <u>evidence</u> for evolution:

Observations of Fossils Can Provide Evidence for Evolution

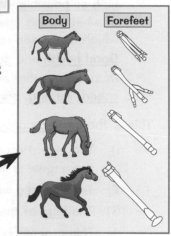

1) A fossil is <u>any trace</u> of an animal or plant that lived <u>long</u> ago. They are most commonly found in <u>rocks</u>.

2) They can tell us a lot about what the organisms <u>looked like</u> and <u>how long ago</u> they existed. Generally, the <u>deeper</u> the rock, the <u>older</u> the fossil.

3) By arranging fossils in <u>chronological</u> (date) order, <u>gradual changes</u> in organisms can be observed. This provides <u>evidence</u> for <u>evolution</u>, because it shows how species have <u>changed</u> and <u>developed</u> over many years. For example, if you look at the <u>fossilised bones</u> of a <u>horse</u>, you can put together a family tree to suggest how the modern horse might have <u>evolved</u>.

Bacteria Can Show Evolution As it Happens

1) Like all organisms, bacteria sometimes develop <u>random mutations</u> in their DNA, which introduces new <u>variants</u> into the population. These can lead to <u>changes</u> in the bacteria's <u>phenotype</u> — for example, a bacterium could become <u>less affected</u> by a particular <u>antibiotic</u> (a substance designed to kill bacteria or prevent them from reproducing).

2) For the bacterium, this ability to resist antibiotics is a big <u>advantage</u>. The bacterium is better able to <u>survive</u>, even in a host who's being treated with antibiotics, and so it <u>lives for longer</u> and <u>reproduces</u> many more times.

One way that bacteria might be resistant to an antibiotic is if they have an enzyme that can break the antibiotic down.

3) This leads to the <u>resistant variant</u> being <u>passed on</u> to offspring and becoming more and more common over time — it's just <u>natural selection</u>.

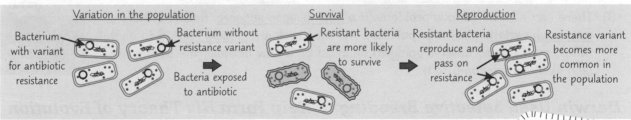

4) As with any <u>scientific theory</u>, scientists continue to <u>test</u> the theory of evolution by natural selection by making <u>new observations</u> and <u>collecting new evidence</u>. The emergence of antibiotic-resistant bacteria can be <u>explained</u> by the theory of evolution by natural selection (as there is change in the inherited characteristics of a population over time). What's more, because bacteria reproduce <u>very quickly</u>, scientists can observe evolution <u>as it's occurring</u>, so it provides great <u>support</u> for the theory.

The theory of natural selection was developed by Charles Darwin (see page 89).

5) It's due to strong evidence like this that the theory of evolution by natural selection is now widely <u>accepted</u> by the <u>scientific community</u>.

The fossil record — it rocks...

Life on Earth is still evolving — the evidence is right under our feet and under our microscopes.

Q1 How do genetic variants for antibiotic resistance arise in a population of bacteria? [1 mark]

Q2 Describe how fossils provide evidence for evolution. [2 marks]

Selective Breeding

So, you know that organisms change through evolution by <u>natural selection</u>, but <u>humans</u> can also cause organisms to change, through the process of <u>selective breeding</u>.

Selective Breeding is Mating the Best Organisms to Get Good Offspring

Humans use selective breeding to develop <u>new varieties</u> of organisms with <u>beneficial</u> <u>characteristics</u> for human use. For example, organisms can be bred to have:

- A <u>maximum yield</u> of meat, milk, grain, etc. — this means that food production is <u>as high as possible</u>, which is very important for <u>food security</u> (see p.96). In fact, <u>most</u> of what we eat nowadays comes from organisms which have been selectively bred.
- <u>Good health</u> and <u>disease resistance</u>.
- In animals, other qualities like <u>temperament</u>, <u>speed</u>, <u>fertility</u>, <u>good mothering skills</u>, etc.

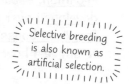

This is the <u>basic process</u> involved in selective breeding:

1) The parent organisms with the <u>best characteristics</u> are selected, e.g. the largest sheep and rams — those with the highest meat yield.

2) They're <u>bred</u> with each other.

3) The <u>best</u> of the <u>offspring</u> are selected and <u>bred</u>.

4) This process is repeated over several generations to develop the <u>desired traits</u>, e.g. to produce sheep with very large meat yields.

Selective breeding is also known as artificial selection.

Selective Breeding Causes a Reduction in the Gene Pool

1) Although selective breeding can be very useful for humans, the main problem with it is that it reduces the <u>gene pool</u> — the <u>number</u> of different <u>genetic variants</u> (alleles) in a population. This is because the farmer keeps breeding from the "<u>best</u>" animals or plants — which are all <u>closely related</u>. This is known as <u>inbreeding</u>.

2) Inbreeding can cause <u>health problems</u> because there's more chance of the organisms developing <u>harmful genetic disorders</u> when the <u>gene pool</u> is <u>limited</u>.

3) There can also be serious problems if a <u>new disease appears</u>, because there's <u>not much variation</u> in the population. All the stock are <u>closely related</u> to each other, so if one of them is going to be killed by a new disease, the others are <u>also</u> likely to succumb to it.

Darwin Used Selective Breeding to Help Form His Theory of Evolution

1) Selective breeding's not a new thing. People have been doing it for <u>hundreds of years</u>. In fact, it helped <u>Charles Darwin</u> (see next page) come up with his <u>theory of evolution by natural selection</u>.

2) He noticed that the selective breeding of plants and animals had created <u>different varieties</u> of species, and that these <u>new</u> varieties were sometimes <u>very different</u> from the original '<u>wild</u>' version of the species they had <u>descended</u> from.

3) He started to question whether <u>natural processes</u> (rather than humans) somehow <u>selected</u> individuals with traits that made them more likely to <u>survive</u> in a particular environment, and whether this could be the reason for the <u>variety</u> of different organisms, and the <u>creation</u> of <u>new species</u>, on Earth.

I use the same genes all the time too — they flatter my hips...

The basic process of selective breeding has stayed the same over many years — select the best individuals, let them reproduce, repeat over many generations, and voilà...

Q1   A farmer who grows green beans lives in an area that experiences a lot of drought. Explain how he could use selective breeding to improve the chances of his bean plants surviving the droughts.   [3 marks]

Darwin and Wallace

Darwin and Wallace were scientists working more than 150 years ago. Little did they know we'd still be harping on about their ideas today...

Darwin Brought Together a Lot of Evidence for his Theory of Evolution

Charles Darwin is well known as the guy who came up with the theory of evolution by natural selection. The development of the theory is a good example of how scientific theories arise. Darwin made observations, collected evidence, looked at the work of other scientists to check and improve his explanations, then shared his theory with the scientific community. This is how he did it:

1) He spent 5 years on a voyage around the world studying plants and animals as well as any fossils that he found.

2) He made many observations about the similarities and differences between fossils and living organisms, as well as between the organisms of different islands.

3) He noticed that there was variation in members of the same species and that those with characteristics most suited to their environment were more likely to survive.

Charles Darwin

4) He also noticed that characteristics could be passed on to offspring.

5) Back in England, he carried out selective breeding experiments (see previous page) to show how selection of particular characteristics could lead to the development of new varieties of an organism.

6) Alfred Russel Wallace was a scientist working at the same time as Darwin — he also made observations about organisms and came up with the idea of natural selection, independently of Darwin.

7) Wallace also proposed that evolution by natural selection might lead to the development of new species if populations of the same species become isolated from each other and live in different ecosystems.

8) Wallace and Darwin published their papers on evolution together and acknowledged each other's work. But it was Darwin's famous book 'On the Origin of Species' (published in 1859) that made other scientists pay attention to the theory. This book is partly why Darwin is usually better remembered than Wallace.

Ideas About Evolution have Influenced Modern Biology

That Darwin chap was right...

1) As scientists have discovered more about DNA, the evidence for Darwin's theory has become even stronger — e.g. we now know that mutations cause genetic variants which can be inherited and cause variation in a population.

2) The acceptance of the theory of evolution by natural selection has affected lots of different areas of biology and society, including:

- classification — if all living organisms have descended from a common ancestor, then we're all related in some way. We now classify organisms (arrange them into groups) based on how closely related they are (see page 91).

- antibiotic resistance — we now understand the importance of finishing the course of drugs to prevent resistant bacteria spreading (see page 87) and we know we need to constantly develop new antibiotics to fight newly evolved resistant bacteria.

- conservation — we now understand the importance of genetic variation and how it helps populations adapt to changing environments. This has led to conservation projects to protect species (see p.93).

3) However, the theory of evolution by natural selection is often misunderstood, and many people are not aware of the evidence for it. There are also some people who simply don't believe in it — this is often due to religious beliefs.

Darwin was a darlin', and Wallace was well ace...

Biology wouldn't be what it is today without Darwin and Wallace, but at the time, their ideas were revolutionary.

Q1   Describe two observations made by Darwin that helped him to develop his theory of evolution.   [2 marks]

Asexual and Sexual Reproduction

Reproducing is <u>very important</u> to all organisms — it's how they <u>pass on</u> their <u>genes</u> to the next generation. How easy it is for a population or species to <u>evolve</u> partly depends on the way they reproduce.

Asexual and Sexual Reproduction Have Advantages and Disadvantages

1) Some organisms reproduce <u>sexually</u>, some reproduce <u>asexually</u>, and some can do <u>both</u>.

2) Cells can reproduce <u>asexually</u>, e.g. by dividing by <u>mitosis</u> — this results in <u>two daughter cells</u>, which are genetically <u>identical</u> to each other and to the parent cell (see page 59).

3) <u>Sexual reproduction</u> involves <u>meiosis</u> and the production of <u>genetically different</u> gametes, which fuse to form a zygote at <u>fertilisation</u> (see page 62).

4) You need to be able to explain some of the <u>advantages</u> and <u>disadvantages</u> of asexual and sexual reproduction. For example:

<table>
<tr><th></th><th>ASEXUAL REPRODUCTION</th><th>SEXUAL REPRODUCTION</th></tr>
<tr>
<td rowspan="2">ADVANTAGES</td>
<td>
• Asexual reproduction can produce <u>lots</u> of offspring <u>very quickly</u> because the <u>reproductive cycle</u> (the time it takes to produce independent offspring) is so <u>fast</u>.
• For example, the bacteria E. coli can divide <u>every 20 minutes</u> in the lab.
• This can allow organisms to <u>colonise a new area</u> very <u>rapidly</u>.
</td>
<td rowspan="2">
• Sexual reproduction creates <u>genetic variation</u> within the population, which means different individuals have <u>different characteristics</u>.
• This means that if the environmental conditions <u>change</u>, it's <u>more likely</u> that at least <u>some individuals</u> in the population will have the characteristics to <u>survive</u> the change.
• Over time this leads to <u>evolution</u>, as species become <u>better adapted</u> to their new environment.
</td>
</tr>
<tr>
<td>
• Only <u>one parent</u> is needed — this means organisms can reproduce whenever conditions are <u>favourable</u>, <u>without</u> having to wait for a <u>mate</u>.
• For example, aphids reproduce asexually during <u>summer</u> when there is <u>plenty of food</u>.
</td>
</tr>
<tr>
<td rowspan="2">DISADVANTAGES</td>
<td rowspan="2">
• There's <u>no genetic variation</u> between offspring in the population — all individuals are <u>genetically identical</u>.
• So, if the <u>environment changes</u> and conditions become <u>unfavourable</u>, the <u>whole population</u> may be affected.
• For example, Black Sigatoka is a disease that affects <u>banana</u> plants, which reproduce <u>asexually</u>. So, if there's an outbreak of the <u>disease</u>, it's likely that <u>all</u> banana plants in the population will be <u>affected</u> as there are <u>none</u> that are <u>resistant</u> to it.
</td>
<td>
• Sexual reproduction takes more <u>time</u> and <u>energy</u> than asexual reproduction, so organisms produce <u>fewer offspring</u> in their lifetime.
• For example, organisms need to <u>find</u> and <u>attract</u> mates, which takes time and energy. E.g. male bowerbirds <u>build</u> structures out of twigs and then <u>dance</u> to impress females.
</td>
</tr>
<tr>
<td>
• <u>Two parents</u> are needed for sexual reproduction. This can be a problem if individuals are <u>isolated</u>.
• For example, polar bears often live <u>alone</u>, so male polar bears may have to walk up to <u>100 miles</u> to find a mate.
</td>
</tr>
</table>

Asexual reproduction — an aphid's answer to life in the fast lane...

So, both sexual and asexual reproduction have their pros and cons — which is why some organisms can do both.

Q1 Strawberry plants can reproduce asexually.
Explain one disadvantage of this form of reproduction. [2 marks]

Classification

It seems to be a basic human urge to want to classify things — that's the case in biology anyway...

Classification is Organising Living Organisms into Groups

1) Traditionally, organisms were classified according to similarities and differences in their observable characteristics, i.e. things you can see (like how many legs something has). As technology improved, this included things you can see with a microscope, e.g. cell structure.

2) These characteristics were used to classify organisms in the five kingdom classification system. In this system, living things are first divided into five groups called kingdoms (e.g. the plant kingdom, the animal kingdom).

3) The kingdoms are then subdivided into smaller and smaller groups that have common features — phylum, class, order, family, genus, species.

Developments in Biology Lead to Improvements in Classification

1) The five kingdom classification system is still used, but it's now a bit out of date.

2) Over time, technology has developed further and our understanding of things like biochemical processes and genetics has increased. This has resulted in new discoveries being made and the relationships between organisms being clarified.

3) For example, DNA analysis allows scientists to find out the differences between organisms, even if the organisms are physically very similar to each other.

- Scientists can use DNA sequencing to compare particular genes or entire genomes of different organisms, using only small samples of tissue.
- They look for similarities, e.g. if the different species share the same number of genes, or a similar number of genetic variants for a particular gene.
- If different organisms share the same number of genes or genetic variants for a gene, then they are likely to have inherited these similarities from a common ancestor.
- The more similar the DNA sequences between species, the more closely related they are and the more likely it is that they'll be classified in the same group. E.g. the base sequence for human and chimpanzee DNA is about 94% the same, so humans and chimpanzees are closely related to each other.

An organism's genome is all of its genetic material.

4) Scientists can also use DNA sequences to estimate how long ago two species separated from each other.

5) This is because genetic variants arise by mutations and scientists have estimates for how frequently these mutations can happen.

6) By finding the number of different genetic variants between two species, scientists can estimate when speciation (the emergence of new species) occurred.

Evolutionary Trees Show How Species are Related to Each Other

1) Scientists can use classification data to join species together in evolutionary trees.

2) In an evolutionary tree, species are connected to each other by lines via their most recent common ancestor. This helps to show their relationship to each other.

3) The more closely related two species are to each other, the fewer the number of steps between them on the tree.

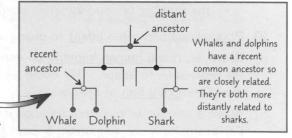

Whales and dolphins have a recent common ancestor so are closely related. They're both more distantly related to sharks.

My brother's been reclassified — he's back with the apes...

As new techniques enable us to study organisms at the level of their genes, our classification systems get better.

Q1 Suggest one limitation of classifying organisms based only on their physical characteristics. [1 mark]

Biodiversity

Time for something less joyous. We <u>humans</u> can have some <u>really damaging negative impacts</u> on ecosystems...

Biodiversity is all About the Variety of Life in an Area

<u>Biodiversity</u> is a combination of <u>three different factors</u>. These are:
- the diversity (variety) of <u>living organisms</u> in a particular area.
- the diversity of different <u>genes</u> and <u>alleles</u> in a particular area (also known as <u>genetic diversity</u>).
- the diversity of different <u>ecosystems</u> in a particular area.

A <u>high level</u> of biodiversity (whether globally or just in a small area) is a good thing — it means that if the environment <u>changes</u> in some way, there's a good chance that at least <u>some species and ecosystems</u> will be able to <u>survive</u>. It also means that we <u>humans</u> can get the most out of the <u>world's resources</u> (see p.95).

Human Interactions Can Reduce Biodiversity

1) Like all organisms, we humans have an <u>impact</u> on the <u>ecosystems around us</u>. The impact humans have on ecosystems has <u>changed a lot</u> in the last couple of centuries. This is largely due to:

> 1) An <u>increasing human population</u> — the human population on Earth has grown <u>hugely</u> over the last 200 years and is <u>continuing</u> to rise. Many more people on the planet means we need to take up <u>more land</u> and use <u>more resources</u> in order to <u>survive</u>.
>
> 2) <u>Industrialisation</u> — due to improvements in <u>technology</u> and the need for more <u>goods</u> and <u>services</u>, there is now much more <u>industry</u> on the planet than there was a couple of centuries ago. This means we are using <u>more raw materials</u> (e.g. oil, wood) and <u>more energy</u> to <u>manufacture goods</u>. It also means we're creating <u>more waste products</u>, which can lead to <u>more pollution</u>.
>
> 3) <u>Globalisation</u> — as <u>communication</u> and <u>transport</u> have improved, different countries have become more <u>connected</u> with each other. This means that countries are able to <u>buy</u> and <u>sell</u> products from each other more easily and the <u>same companies</u> are able to operate in <u>several different countries</u>.

2) These changes can <u>damage</u> or <u>destroy</u> ecosystems and can <u>reduce</u> biodiversity. Here are a few reasons why:

> 1) <u>Habitat destruction</u> — <u>human activities</u> (e.g. farming, building, quarrying) reduce the amount of <u>land</u> and <u>resources</u> available to <u>other</u> animals and plants, which can reduce <u>biodiversity</u> in an area. For example, <u>woodland</u> may be <u>cleared</u> for farmland and can result in a <u>reduction</u> in the number of <u>tree species</u>, so reducing <u>biodiversity</u>. It also destroys the <u>habitats</u> of other organisms — species will <u>die</u> or be forced to <u>migrate</u> elsewhere, further reducing biodiversity.
>
> 2) <u>Waste</u> — the <u>increasing population</u> and <u>industrialisation</u> means we're producing more waste, which can <u>damage ecosystems</u> in many ways. For example, <u>sewage</u> and <u>toxic chemicals</u> from <u>industry</u> and <u>agriculture</u> can pollute lakes, rivers and oceans, affecting the plants and animals that rely on them for <u>survival</u> (including humans).
>
> 3) <u>Sharing resources</u> — increasing <u>globalisation</u> (see above) means that resources can be <u>shared</u> between many countries. Unfortunately, this can lead to a loss of <u>biodiversity</u>. For example, large companies can sell the 'best' varieties of seeds to farmers in many different countries, reducing the <u>number</u> of seed varieties used for crops <u>globally</u> and therefore reducing <u>global biodiversity</u>.

3) Populations can often <u>adapt</u> to changes in the environment through <u>evolution</u> by <u>natural selection</u>.

4) However, many <u>human impacts</u> on ecosystems take place so <u>quickly</u> that there is not <u>enough time</u> for organisms to adapt. This could lead to the <u>loss of populations</u> of species from an area or even the complete <u>extinction</u> of species.

5) When a species is lost from an ecosystem it can have <u>knock-on effects</u> for other organisms. For example, it can negatively impact <u>food chains</u>, which could cause a <u>further decrease</u> in biodiversity.

I'm sorry but I'd prefer it if biodiversity was low inside my house...

Industrialisation and globalisation may be useful for us, but unfortunately it tends to be bad news for biodiversity.

Q1   Explain one way in which chemicals used in agriculture may lead to a loss in biodiversity.   [2 marks]

More on Biodiversity

You've seen on the last page how humans can have a negative effect on biodiversity, so now for some positivity. Here's how humans can help to prevent the loss of biodiversity and preserve it for future generations.

Humans Can Use Resources Sustainably

1) Sustainability means meeting the needs of today's population without harming the environment or using up resources, so that future generations can still meet their own needs. Using resources sustainably means that the rate at which we use resources is not greater than the rate at which they are replaced.

> For example, sustainable harvesting of timber may involve the replanting of trees after harvesting so that new trees replace the ones that are cut.

2) Sustainability means humans will have less of a negative impact on ecosystems and biodiversity.

Conservation Schemes Can Protect Biodiversity

Conservation schemes can help to protect biodiversity by conserving species or their habitats. This can be done on several different levels. For example:

Protecting specific species

1) Specific species can be protected in their natural habitat, e.g. by banning the hunting of some species.

2) Species can also be protected by being kept in safe areas, away from harmful activities such as hunting or habitat destruction. For animals, safe areas include zoos and for plants they include botanical gardens and seed banks (large collections of seeds from many different plant species). Breeding programmes in captivity can also increase the number of a species before releasing them back into the wild.

Protecting habitats and ecosystems

1) Setting aside specific protected areas helps to conserve entire habitats and ecosystems by restricting the development of the land — e.g. for building houses and farming.

2) Protected areas include places like national parks and nature reserves. They can also be found in the sea where human activities like fishing are controlled to protect marine ecosystems.

Preventing ecosystem damage on a global scale

1) Some human activities, such as burning fossil fuels, are increasing the level of greenhouse gases in the atmosphere, which is contributing to global warming (the gradual warming up of the planet).

2) Global warming is a type of climate change and causes other types of climate change, e.g. changing rainfall patterns.

3) Climate change could reduce biodiversity on Earth — e.g. some species may be unable to survive a change in the climate, so become extinct.

4) So, in order to protect global biodiversity, it may be necessary to control human activities in order to reduce greenhouse gas emissions.

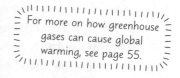
For more on how greenhouse gases can cause global warming, see page 55.

My room is a protected area from the species Brother horribilis...

So, there you go — it's not all doom and gloom. There are lots of things that we can do to help biodiversity — we just have to hurry up if we want as many species as possible to survive in the future.

Q1 The Siberian tiger is an endangered species. Explain how zoos could help to increase the number of Siberian tigers in the wild.

[2 marks]

Biodiversity and The Distribution of Organisms

Sometimes it can be difficult to assess the biodiversity within an area because it doesn't just <u>stay the same</u> all the time. This page is all about why biodiversity might <u>change</u> and how you can <u>interpret data</u> on it.

Environmental Changes Affect The Distribution of Organisms

1) <u>Environmental changes</u> can cause the <u>distribution of organisms</u> to change. A change in distribution means a change in <u>where</u> an organism <u>lives</u>,

2) Environmental changes that can affect organisms in this way include:

  • A change in the AVAILABILITY of WATER. For example:

   > The <u>distribution</u> of some <u>animal</u> and <u>plant species</u> in the <u>tropics</u> changes between the <u>wet</u> and the <u>dry</u> seasons — i.e. the times of year where there is more or less <u>rainfall</u>, and so more or less <u>water available</u>. E.g. each year in Africa, large numbers of <u>giant wildebeest migrate</u>, moving <u>north</u> and then back <u>south</u> as the <u>rainfall patterns change</u>.

  • A change in ATMOSPHERIC GASES. For example:

   > The distribution of some species <u>changes</u> in areas where there is more <u>air pollution</u>. E.g. some species of <u>lichen</u> can't grow in areas where <u>sulfur dioxide</u> is given out by certain <u>industrial processes</u>.

   See p.47 for more on lichens and how they can be used to indicate how polluted the air is in an area.

3) These environmental changes can be caused by <u>seasonal</u> factors, <u>geographic</u> factors or <u>human interaction</u>.

4) A change in the distribution of organisms can affect biodiversity as it affects the variety of living organisms in an area.

You Might Have to Interpret Data on Biodiversity

There are lots of ways of <u>illustrating</u> the biodiversity of an area. In the exam, you might need to <u>interpret</u> data on biodiversity that's presented in a <u>chart</u>, <u>graph</u> or <u>table</u>. Here's an example:

1) Scientists counted the <u>number</u> of different lichen species found on <u>gravestones</u> at different <u>distances</u> from a city centre. The results are shown on the graph.

2) You might need to interpret the graph and <u>read a value</u> from it. E.g. you could be asked, 'At <u>what distance</u> from the city centre was the <u>greatest lichen biodiversity</u> recorded?'. The place with the greatest lichen biodiversity would be where the greatest <u>number</u> of <u>different</u> lichen species was recorded. From the graph you can see that the greatest number of different lichen species (35) was recorded at <u>24 km</u> from the city centre.

3) You could be asked to interpret the graph to describe the <u>relationship</u> between lichen <u>biodiversity</u> and <u>distance</u> from the city centre. You know that <u>fewer</u> lichen species indicate a <u>lower</u> biodiversity, so your answer could be, 'Lichen biodiversity is <u>positively correlated</u> with distance from the city centre'. (Because as lichen biodiversity increases, so does distance from the city centre.)

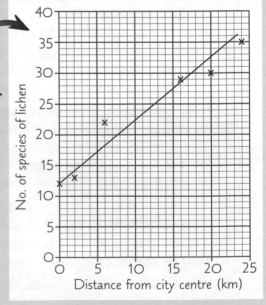

A release of gas often affects the distribution of people in a room...

Being able to assess the biodiversity of an area can be important for identifying parts of the world which should be priorities for conservation schemes — e.g. places with lots of different species. So it's important that scientists can interpret data on biodiversity and understand how it can be affected by environmental changes.

Q1   Give two environmental changes that can affect the distribution of living organisms.   [2 marks]

Maintaining Biodiversity

Trying to preserve biodiversity can be <u>tricky</u> but there are <u>benefits</u> for doing it, so it's <u>pretty worthwhile</u>...

Maintaining Biodiversity Benefits Wildlife and Humans

Humans, like all other organisms, depend on other organisms for their <u>survival</u>, e.g. for things such as <u>food</u> and <u>shelter</u>. So, as well as benefitting <u>endangered species</u>, maintaining biodiversity often helps <u>humans</u> too:

1) <u>Protecting the human food supply</u> — over-fishing has <u>greatly reduced fish stocks</u> in the world's oceans. Conservation programmes can ensure that future generations will have <u>fish to eat</u>.

2) <u>Ensuring minimal damage to food chains</u> — if <u>one species</u> becomes <u>extinct</u> it will affect all the organisms that feed on and are eaten by that species, so the <u>whole food chain</u> is affected. This means <u>conserving one species</u> may <u>help others</u> to survive.

3) <u>Providing future medicines</u> — many of the medicines we use today come from <u>plants</u>. Undiscovered plant species may contain <u>new medicinal chemicals</u>. If these plants are allowed to become <u>extinct</u>, perhaps through <u>rainforest destruction</u>, we could miss out on valuable medicines.

4) <u>Providing industrial materials and fuels</u> — plant and animal species are involved in the production of <u>industrial materials</u> (e.g. wood, paper, adhesives and oils) and some <u>fuels</u>. If these species become extinct these important resources may become <u>more difficult</u> to produce.

Maintaining Biodiversity can be Challenging

Ways of maintaining biodiversity are <u>great in theory</u> but they can be <u>difficult</u> to do in the real world, whether at a <u>local</u> or <u>global</u> level. Many factors have to be considered before <u>deciding</u> to go ahead with conservation schemes. Here are a few examples of why:

Economic issues

1) It can be <u>expensive</u> to conserve species or habitats. The <u>cost</u> of a conservation scheme has to be weighed against the <u>potential benefits</u> of maintaining biodiversity.

2) Many developing countries are rich in <u>natural resources</u>, e.g. <u>Ecuador</u> is a developing country with many <u>biodiverse</u> areas, however it also has large reserves of <u>petroleum</u>. <u>Accessing</u> these natural resources and <u>selling</u> them may help to <u>boost</u> the country's <u>economy</u>, but this could also have a <u>negative effect</u> on the country's ecosystems.

Moral issues

1) The <u>conservation</u> of <u>some endangered species</u> may have no <u>obvious benefit</u> for humans (e.g. the Giant Panda), but many people think we should still help to prevent species from becoming <u>extinct</u>.

2) Some people think it's morally wrong to <u>stop</u> humans in developing countries from <u>using</u> natural resources that could <u>boost</u> their <u>economy</u> (see above) in favour of protecting plants and animals.

3) Protecting <u>one</u> species may mean <u>killing</u> individuals of another species, which some people think is wrong, e.g. <u>possums</u> in New Zealand have <u>reduced</u> the numbers of organisms of <u>native</u> species, so there are widespread schemes to <u>kill</u> possums in order to <u>protect</u> native wildlife.

Ecological issues

Ecosystems are very <u>complex</u> — conservation schemes that try to protect <u>one</u> species or habitat could have knock-on effects in <u>other parts</u> of the ecosystem. This means that people have to think very carefully about what <u>future effects</u> conservation schemes could have before they are set up.

Political issues

1) Some conservation schemes require several different countries to <u>work together</u>. This can be difficult if some countries <u>aren't willing</u> to sign up to an agreement. E.g. many countries have signed up to <u>agreements</u> to restrict whaling but there are still some that haven't (e.g. Norway, Japan).

2) On a smaller scale, conservation schemes can be <u>objected to</u> by <u>local communities</u>. E.g. people might not be keen if a local scheme <u>reduces their income</u> (e.g. fishing restrictions in a fishing village).

It's a shame exams aren't an endangered species...

Hmmm, I guess the maintenance of biodiversity can be a bit tricky but if it keeps food on the table I'm keen...

Q1   Explain why maintaining biodiversity could be important for providing medicines in the future.   [2 marks]

Human Food Security

Food security isn't about <u>locking</u> your <u>biscuit tin</u>. Think of it as '<u>securing</u>' enough food to feed everyone.

Not Everyone Has 'Food Security'

1) As you saw on p.92, the world's <u>population</u> is <u>rising very quickly</u>, and it's not slowing down.

2) This means that global <u>food production</u> must <u>increase</u> too, so that we all have access to <u>enough food</u> that is <u>safe for us to eat</u> and has the right balance of <u>nutrition</u> — this is known as '<u>food security</u>'.

3) As well as the <u>rising human population</u>, you need to know about these factors that affect food security:

Environmental change

1) Environmental changes may impact our ability to produce food. For example, changes to the global climate such as <u>increased temperature</u> could affect the <u>growth patterns</u> of crops, which could result in a <u>reduction in yield</u> (the amount of <u>useful</u> product made).

2) Other changes such as <u>pollution</u> could also reduce our ability to grow crops.

Changing diets in wealthier populations

1) As people become <u>wealthier</u>, their diets are likely to change to include a <u>wider variety of foods</u>. An example of this is people <u>eating more meat</u>, which is <u>expensive</u> to buy.

2) This increased demand for meat can be <u>bad</u> for food security. Animals being reared for meat can be <u>fed crops</u> that would otherwise be <u>eaten by humans</u> and <u>graze on land</u> that could be used to <u>grow crops to feed humans</u>.

New pests and pathogens

<u>Pests</u> (e.g. certain insects) and <u>pathogens</u> (e.g. bacteria, fungi and viruses — see p.14) can result in the <u>loss</u> of crops or livestock and could lead to <u>widespread famine</u>.

Sustainability (see page 93)

If we use <u>unsustainable methods</u> to produce food (e.g. farming practices that permanently damage the environment or rely on non-renewable resources), this is likely to <u>negatively impact</u> the level of <u>food security</u>.

Cost of agricultural inputs

1) Agriculture relies on several <u>inputs</u> such as <u>fuel</u>, <u>chemicals</u>, <u>animal feed</u>, etc.

2) The high <u>input costs</u> of farming can make it <u>too expensive</u> for people in some countries to <u>start</u> or <u>maintain food production</u>, meaning that there sometimes <u>aren't</u> enough people producing food to feed everyone.

There are Many Methods for Improving Food Security

Crop or livestock <u>yield</u> can be improved by using a variety of <u>agricultural methods</u>. For example:

1) <u>Improved nutrition</u> — making sure that livestock have access to all of the necessary <u>nutrients</u> for their <u>health</u> and <u>growth</u>. Farmers also use <u>fertilisers</u> on <u>soils</u> to <u>provide</u> elements needed for <u>plant growth</u>.

2) <u>Chemical control of pests</u> — <u>pesticides</u> can be used to reduce <u>damage</u> done by pests, by <u>killing</u> them.

3) <u>Protection against pathogens</u> — livestock may be <u>vaccinated</u> (see page 18) against certain <u>diseases</u> caused by pathogens. <u>Antibiotics</u> can also be given to livestock to <u>protect them</u> against <u>bacterial</u> pathogens.

4) <u>Hormones</u> — <u>plant hormones</u> can be applied to <u>crops</u> to increase food production, e.g. by controlling when they can be <u>harvested</u> or when <u>fruit ripens</u> (see page 65). <u>Livestock</u> can also be given hormones to increase their <u>meat</u> or <u>milk production</u>.

5) <u>Selective breeding</u> — this can be used to create <u>varieties</u> of organisms with high yields (see p.88).

<u>Biotechnology</u> can also be used to increase food production. For example, <u>genetic engineering</u> can create <u>genetically modified crops</u> that are <u>resistant</u> to things such as <u>drought</u>, <u>insects</u>, certain <u>diseases</u> and <u>herbicides</u>.

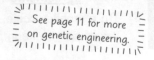
See page 11 for more on genetic engineering.

Food insecurity — potatoes with a lack of self-confidence...

Global food security is a big task for the future, but it might be tricky to balance it with maintaining biodiversity.

Q1   Describe how the outbreak of a new crop pathogen could impact the level of food security.   [2 marks]

Revision Questions for Chapter B6

Good work — now you should know all about how <u>life evolved</u> and how we should <u>protect</u> it in the <u>future</u>.

- Try these questions and <u>tick off each one</u> when you <u>get it right</u>.
- When you've done <u>all the questions</u> for a topic and are <u>completely happy</u> with it, tick off the topic.

Natural Selection and Evolution (p.86-87) ☑

1) How likely is it that a genetic variant will have a really big effect on an organism's phenotype? ☑
2) Describe how organisms evolve by the process of natural selection. ☑
3) Define 'evolution'. ☑
4) Explain how speciation can occur when two populations of a species are isolated. ☑
5) What is a fossil? ☑
6) Other than fossils, give one other example of evidence which shows that species evolve over time. ☑

Selective Breeding and Darwin and Wallace (p.88-89) ☑

7) What is selective breeding? ☑
8) Give one disadvantage of selective breeding. ☑
9) Describe one way in which Wallace contributed to the theory of evolution by natural selection. ☑
10) Describe one way in which the theory of evolution by natural selection has influenced modern biology. ☑
11) Give one reason why some people do not accept the theory of evolution by natural selection. ☑

Asexual and Sexual Reproduction and Classification (p.90-91) ☑

12) How many parents are needed for asexual reproduction? ☑
13) Explain why organisms that reproduce sexually may produce fewer offspring in their lifetime than those that reproduce asexually. ☑
14) What does classification mean? ☑
15) Explain how DNA analysis helps scientists to classify organisms. ☑

Biodiversity and the Distribution of Organisms (p.92-95) ☑

16) What is meant by biodiversity? ☑
17) Explain one way in which globalisation can reduce global biodiversity. ☑
18) Describe one way in which humans can conserve a specific species. ☑
19) Explain why conservation schemes to protect global biodiversity might aim to reduce the amount of fossil fuels we burn. ☑
20) Explain how a change in atmospheric gases may affect biodiversity within an ecosystem. ☑
21) Give one advantage to humans of maintaining biodiversity. ☑
22) Describe one moral issue which may be discussed when deciding on schemes to protect biodiversity. ☑
23) Give an example of a political issue that could challenge the success of a conservation scheme. ☑

Human Food Security (p.96) ☑

24) What is meant by food security? ☑
25) How may an increased temperature threaten food security in the future? ☑
26) Describe how hormones can be used in agriculture to improve crop yields. ☑
27) Give one biotechnological method which can be used to improve crop yields. ☑

The Scientific Method

Coming up with a new <u>scientific theory</u> is easier said than done — it's an almost never-ending <u>cycle</u> of collecting <u>data</u>, <u>analysing</u> it, reaching a <u>conclusion</u>, improving your <u>method</u>, collecting more <u>data</u>... etc. etc.

Scientists Come Up With Hypotheses — Then Test Them

1) Scientists try to <u>explain</u> things (and explain them <u>really well</u>). There <u>isn't</u> a <u>single</u> scientific <u>method</u> that all scientists use to do this, but scientists do follow certain <u>conventions</u> and scientific <u>principles</u>.

2) They usually start by <u>observing</u> or <u>thinking about</u> something they don't understand.
    They then try to come up with a <u>hypothesis</u>:

    - A hypothesis <u>isn't</u> just a <u>summary</u> of observations (e.g. light intensity affects rate of photosynthesis).

    - It's a <u>tentative explanation</u> for it (e.g. light intensity affects the rate of photosynthesis <u>because</u> light is needed to provide energy for photosynthesis).

    - Observations made by scientists are just that — observations. They <u>don't show</u> what the hypothesis should be. In order to come up with a decent explanation for their observations, scientists need to <u>use their imagination</u>.

    - A good hypothesis should account for <u>all</u> of the observations made and any other <u>available data</u> (i.e. what's already been observed). If it doesn't, it's not really a very good explanation.

3) The next step is to <u>test</u> whether the hypothesis might be <u>right or not</u>. This involves making a <u>prediction</u> based on the hypothesis — i.e. stating how <u>changing</u> a particular <u>factor</u> will affect the <u>outcome</u> of a situation. The prediction is then tested by <u>gathering evidence</u> (i.e. <u>data</u>) from <u>investigations</u>.

    For example, a scientist might predict that an <u>increase</u> in <u>light intensity</u> will <u>increase</u> the <u>rate</u> of <u>photosynthesis</u>. This prediction could be <u>written</u> as a <u>statement</u>, or it could be presented <u>visually</u> as a <u>diagram</u> or <u>sketch graph</u>.

    Investigations must be designed so data can be collected in a safe, repeatable, accurate way — see pages 100-101.

4) If <u>evidence</u> from well-conducted <u>experiments</u> backs up a prediction, it <u>increases confidence</u> in the <u>hypothesis</u> — in other words, people are more likely to believe that the hypothesis is true. It <u>doesn't prove</u> a hypothesis is <u>correct</u> though — evidence could still be found that <u>disagrees</u> with it.

5) If the experimental evidence <u>doesn't fit</u> with the hypothesis, then either those <u>results</u> or the <u>hypothesis</u> must be <u>wrong</u> — this <u>decreases confidence</u> in the hypothesis.

6) Sometimes a hypothesis will account for all the data and still turn out to be <u>wrong</u> — that's why every hypothesis needs to be <u>tested</u> further (see the next page).

Different Scientists Can Come Up With Different Explanations

1) Different scientists can make the <u>same observations</u> and come up with <u>different explanations</u> for them — and both these explanations might be perfectly <u>good</u> ones. It's the same with <u>data</u> — two scientists can look at the same data and explain it differently.

2) This is because you need to <u>interpret</u> the thing you're observing (or your data) to come up with an explanation for it — and different people often interpret things in different ways.

3) Sometimes a scientist's <u>personal background</u>, <u>experience</u> or <u>interests</u> will influence the way he or she thinks. For example, a trained geneticist might lean towards a genetic explanation for a disease, but someone else might think it's more about the environment.

4) In these situations, it's important to <u>test</u> the explanations as much as possible — to see which one is most likely to be true (or whether it's a combination of both).

5) Our ability to test explanations has improved as <u>technology has developed</u>. That's because technology allows us make <u>new observations</u> and find <u>new evidence</u>. For example, we now have a better understanding of <u>brain function</u> thanks to the development of machines such as <u>fMRI scanners</u> (see p.73).

6) New data can cause scientists to <u>modify</u> their ideas and <u>hypotheses</u> to fit. E.g.

    When <u>Charles Darwin</u> first came up with the <u>theory of evolution</u> by natural selection (see p.89) <u>DNA</u> and <u>genes hadn't been discovered</u>, so Darwin couldn't explain exactly how characteristics were passed on — those details were <u>added</u> to the theory <u>later on</u>.

The Scientific Method

Several Scientists Will Test a Hypothesis

1) Traditionally, new scientific explanations are announced in peer-reviewed journals, or at scientific conferences.

> A peer-reviewed journal is one where other scientists check results and scientific explanations before the journal is published. They check that people have been 'scientific' about what they're saying (e.g. that experiments have been done in a sensible way). But this doesn't mean that the findings are correct, just that they're not wrong in any obvious kind of way.

2) Once other scientists have found out about a hypothesis, they'll start to base their own predictions on it and carry out their own experiments.

3) When other scientists test the new hypothesis they will also try to reproduce the earlier results. Results that can't be reproduced by another scientist aren't very reliable (they're hard to trust) and scientists tend to be pretty sceptical about them.

4) When testing a hypothesis, a scientist might get some unexpected results. While these could lead to a change in the hypothesis, they tend to be treated with scepticism until they've been repeated (by the same scientist) and reproduced (by other scientists).

If Evidence Supports a Hypothesis, It's Accepted — for Now

1) If a hypothesis is backed up by evidence from loads of experiments, scientists start to have a lot of confidence in it and accept it as a scientific theory — a widely accepted explanation that can be applied to lots of situations. Our current theories have been tested many times over the years and survived.

2) Once scientists have gone through this process and accepted a theory, they take a lot of persuading to drop it — even if some new data appears that can't be explained using the existing theory.

3) Until a better, more plausible explanation is found (one that can explain both the old and new data), the tried and tested theory is likely to stick around — because it already explains loads of other observations really well. And remember, scientists are always sceptical about new data until it's been proved to be repeatable and reproducible (see above).

Theories Can Involve Different Types of Models

Models are used to explain ideas and make predictions. They pick out the key features of a system or process, and the rules that determine how the different features work together. This means they can be used to make predictions and solve problems. There are different types of models:

- Representational models are simplified descriptions, analogies or pictures of what's going on in real life. For example, the lock and key model of enzyme action is a simplified way of showing how enzymes work (see p.32). It can be used to make predictions about what will happen to the rate of an enzyme-controlled reaction in different conditions, e.g. at extremes of pH.

- Spatial models represent physical space and the position of objects within it. They can be used to predict things like the path that will be taken by a storm.

- Descriptive models are used to describe and explain how things work.

- Mathematical models use patterns found in data from past events (and known scientific relationships) to predict what might happen in the future. They require lots of calculations, but modern computers can do these very quickly, which is why many mathematical models are now computational.

- Computational models are mathematical models that use computers. They often involve simulations of complex real-life processes, e.g. climate change.

Models sometimes allow scientists to investigate real-life situations more quickly than they could using experiments (which may also have ethical or practical limitations). However, all models have limitations on what they can explain or predict. For example, climate change models have several limitations — it's hard to take into account all the biological and chemical processes that influence climate. It can also be difficult to include regional variations in climate.

I'm off to the zoo to test my hippo-thesis...

There's an awful lot to take in here. Make sure you understand it all before moving on as it's really important stuff.

Designing Investigations

Dig out your lab coat and dust down your badly-scratched safety goggles... it's <u>investigation time</u>.

Investigations Produce Evidence to Support or Disprove a Hypothesis

1) Scientists <u>observe</u> things and come up with <u>hypotheses</u> to explain them.
   You need to be able to do the same. For example:

   > <u>Observation:</u> People have big feet and spots.
   > <u>Hypothesis:</u> Having big feet causes spots.

   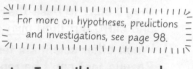
   For more on hypotheses, predictions and investigations, see page 98.

2) Then you carry out an <u>investigation</u> to gather <u>evidence</u> for your hypothesis. To do this, you need to use your hypothesis to make a <u>prediction</u>, e.g. people who have <u>bigger</u> feet will have more spots.

3) Investigations are used to see if there are <u>patterns</u> or <u>relationships</u> between <u>two variables</u>, e.g. to see if there's a pattern or relationship between the variables 'number of spots' and 'size of feet'. You can also carry out investigations to <u>check someone else's data</u>.

   > Investigations include experiments and studies.

Evidence Needs to be Repeatable, Reproducible and Valid

> You'll need to know all the scientific terms on this page, so make sure you understand and learn them.

1) <u>Repeatable</u> means that if the <u>same person</u> does an experiment again using the <u>same methods</u> and equipment, they'll get <u>similar results</u>.

2) <u>Reproducible</u> means that if <u>someone else</u> does the experiment, or a <u>different</u> method or piece of equipment is used, the results will still be <u>similar</u>.

3) If data is <u>repeatable</u> and <u>reproducible</u>, it's <u>reliable</u> and scientists are more likely to <u>have confidence</u> in it.

4) <u>Valid results</u> are both repeatable and reproducible AND they <u>answer the original question</u>. They come from experiments that were designed to be a <u>fair test</u>.

To Make an Investigation a Fair Test You Have to Control the Variables

1) In a lab experiment, you usually <u>change one variable</u> and <u>measure</u> how it affects <u>another variable</u>.

2) To make it a fair test, <u>everything else</u> that could affect the results should <u>stay the same</u> — otherwise you can't tell if the thing you're changing is causing the results or not.

3) The variable you <u>change</u> is called the **INDEPENDENT VARIABLE**.

4) The variable you <u>measure</u> is the **DEPENDENT VARIABLE**.

5) Variables that you <u>keep the same</u> are called **CONTROL VARIABLES**.

   > You could find how <u>temperature</u> affects the rate of an <u>enzyme-controlled reaction</u>.
   > - The <u>independent variable</u> is the <u>temperature</u>.
   > - The <u>dependent variable</u> is the <u>rate of reaction</u>.
   > - <u>Control variables</u> include the <u>concentration</u> and <u>amounts</u> of reactants, <u>pH</u>, the <u>time period</u> you measure, etc.

6) You need to be able to <u>suggest ways to control variables</u> in experiments. For example, you could use a <u>water bath</u> to control the <u>temperature</u> of an enzyme-controlled reaction and a <u>buffer</u> to control <u>pH</u>.

7) Because you can't always control all the variables, you often need to use a <u>control experiment</u>. This is an experiment that's kept under the <u>same conditions</u> as the rest of the investigation, but <u>doesn't</u> have anything <u>done</u> to it. This is so that you can see what happens when you don't change anything at all.

You Can Devise Procedures to Produce or Characterise Substances

You also need to know how to carry out experiments where you <u>produce</u> or <u>characterise</u> a substance. There's lots more information on these in previous chapters. For example, when you carry out an experiment to find the rate of <u>photosynthesis</u> (see p.35), you're <u>producing</u> a substance (<u>oxygen</u>). And when you test for the <u>presence of different biological molecules</u> (see p.52), you're <u>characterising</u> a substance.

Designing Investigations

Investigations Can be Hazardous

1) A <u>hazard</u> is something that can <u>potentially cause harm</u>. Hazards include:

Hmm... Where did my bacteria sample go?

- <u>Microorganisms</u>, e.g. some bacteria can make you ill.
- <u>Chemicals</u>, e.g. sulfuric acid can burn your skin and alcohols catch fire easily.
- <u>Fire</u>, e.g. an unattended Bunsen burner is a fire hazard.
- <u>Electricity</u>, e.g. faulty electrical equipment could give you a shock.

2) Part of planning an investigation is making sure that it's <u>safe</u>.

3) You should always make sure that you <u>identify</u> all the hazards that you might encounter. Then you should think of ways of <u>reducing the risks</u> from the hazards you've identified. For example:

- If you're working with <u>sulfuric acid</u>, always wear gloves and safety goggles. This will reduce the risk of the acid coming into contact with your skin and eyes.
- If you're using a <u>Bunsen burner</u>, stand it on a heat proof mat. This will reduce the risk of starting a fire.

You can find out about potential hazards by looking in textbooks, doing some internet research, or asking your teacher.

The Bigger the Sample Size the Better

Sometimes, your investigation might involve taking samples — in which case you'll need to <u>decide how big</u> your sample size is going to be. There are a couple of things you need to bear in mind:

1) Data based on <u>small samples</u> isn't as good as data based on large samples. A sample should <u>represent</u> the <u>whole population</u> (i.e. it should share as many of the characteristics in the population as possible) — a small sample can't do that as well. It's also harder to spot <u>outliers</u> (see p.102) if your sample size is too small.

2) The <u>bigger</u> the sample size the <u>better</u>, but scientists (and you) have to be <u>realistic</u> when choosing how big. For example, if a scientist were studying how lifestyle affects people's weight, it'd be great to study everyone in the UK (a huge sample), but it'd take ages and cost a bomb. It's more realistic to study a thousand people, with a mixture of ages, gender and race.

Trial Runs Help Figure out the Range and Interval of Variable Values

1) It's a good idea to do a <u>trial run</u> first — a <u>quick version</u> of your experiment. Trial runs are used to figure out the <u>range</u> of variable values used in the proper experiment (the upper and lower limit).

2) If you <u>don't</u> get a <u>change</u> in the dependent variable at the upper values in the trial run, you might <u>narrow</u> the range in the proper experiment. But if you still get a <u>big change</u> at the upper values you might <u>increase</u> the range.

3) And trial runs can be used to figure out the <u>interval</u> (gaps) between the values too. The intervals <u>can't be too small</u> (otherwise the experiment would take ages), or <u>too big</u> (otherwise you might miss something).

For example, if you were investigating how <u>temperature</u> affects the rate of an <u>enzyme-controlled reaction</u>...
- You might do a trial run with a range of 10-50 °C. If there was no reaction at the upper end (e.g. 40-50 °C), you might narrow the range to 10-40 °C for the proper experiment.
- If using 10 °C intervals gives you a big change in the rate of reaction, you might decide to use 5 °C intervals, e.g. 10, 15, 20, 25°C...

This is no high street survey — it's a designer investigation...

Not only do you need to be able to plan your own investigations, you should also be able to look at someone else's plan and decide whether or not it needs improving. Those examiners aren't half demanding.

Chapter B7 — Ideas About Science

Collecting Data

You've designed the perfect investigation — now it's time to get your hands mucky and collect some data.

Your Data Should be Repeatable, Reproducible, Accurate and Precise

1) To check repeatability you need to repeat the readings and check that the results are similar. You need to repeat each reading at least three times.

2) To make sure your results are reproducible you can cross check them by taking a second set of readings with another instrument (or a different observer).

3) Your data also needs to be ACCURATE. Really accurate results are those that are really close to the true answer. The accuracy of your results usually depends on your method — you need to make sure you're measuring the right thing and that you don't miss anything that should be included in the measurements. E.g. estimating the amount of gas released from a reaction by counting the bubbles isn't very accurate because you might miss some of the bubbles and they might have different volumes. It's more accurate to measure the volume of gas released using a gas syringe (see p.113).

4) Your data also needs to be PRECISE. Precise results are ones where the data is all really close to the mean (average) of your repeated results (i.e. not spread out).

Brian's result was a curate.

Repeat	Data set 1	Data set 2
1	12	11
2	14	17
3	13	14
Mean	13	14

Data set 1 is more precise than data set 2.

Your Equipment has to be Right for the Job

1) The measuring equipment you use has to be sensitive enough to measure the changes you're looking for. For example, if you need to measure changes of 1 cm³ you need to use a measuring cylinder that can measure in 1 cm³ steps — it'd be no good trying with one that only measures in 10 cm³ steps.

2) The smallest change a measuring instrument can detect is called its RESOLUTION. E.g. some mass balances have a resolution of 1 g, some have a resolution of 0.1 g, and some are even more sensitive.

3) Also, equipment needs to be calibrated by measuring a known value. If there's a difference between the measured and known value, you can use this to correct the inaccuracy of the equipment.

You Need to Look out for Errors and Outliers

1) The results of your experiment will always vary a bit because of RANDOM ERRORS — unpredictable differences caused by things like human errors in measuring. E.g. the errors you make when reading from a measuring cylinder are random. You have to estimate or round the level when it's between two marks — so sometimes your figure will be a bit above the real one, and sometimes it will be a bit below.

2) You can reduce the effect of random errors by taking repeat readings and finding the mean. This will make your results more precise.

3) If a measurement is wrong by the same amount every time, it's called a SYSTEMATIC ERROR. For example, if you measured from the very end of your ruler instead of from the 0 cm mark every time, all your measurements would be a bit small. Repeating the experiment in the exact same way and calculating a mean won't correct a systematic error.

> If there's no systematic error, then doing repeats and calculating a mean can make your results more accurate.

4) Just to make things more complicated, if a systematic error is caused by using equipment that isn't zeroed properly, it's called a ZERO ERROR. For example, if a mass balance always reads 1 gram before you put anything on it, all your measurements will be 1 gram too heavy.

5) You can compensate for some systematic errors if you know about them though, e.g. if your mass balance always reads 1 gram before you put anything on it you can subtract 1 gram from all your results.

6) Sometimes you get a result that doesn't fit in with the rest at all. This is called an OUTLIER. Investigate it and try to work out what happened. If you can work this out (e.g. you measured or recorded something wrong) you can ignore it when processing your results — otherwise, treat it as real data.

Watch what you say to that mass balance — it's very sensitive...

Weirdly, data can be really precise but not very accurate. For example, a fancy piece of lab equipment might give results that are really precise, but if it's not been calibrated properly those results won't be accurate.

Processing and Presenting Data

Once you've got your <u>data</u>, you need to <u>interpret</u> it. This means doing a bit of <u>maths</u> to make it <u>more useful</u>.

Data Needs to be Organised and Processed

1) Tables are dead useful for <u>recording results</u> and <u>organising data</u>. When you draw a table, <u>use a ruler</u> and make sure <u>each column</u> has a <u>heading</u> (including the <u>units</u>).

2) When you've done repeats of an experiment, you should calculate the <u>mean</u> (a type of average). To do this <u>add together</u> all the data values and <u>divide by</u> the total number of values in the sample.

You should also be able to calculate the median and mode (two more types of average).

3) You might also need to calculate the <u>range</u>. To do this find the <u>largest</u> number and <u>subtract</u> the <u>smallest</u> number from it. The range is a measure of how <u>spread out</u> the data is. The bigger the range, the less precise the data (and so the less confidence you can have in it).

EXAMPLE: The results of an experiment to find the volume of gas produced in an enzyme-controlled reaction are shown below. Calculate the mean volume and the range.

Repeat 1 (cm³)	Repeat 2 (cm³)	Repeat 3 (cm³)	Mean (cm³)	Range (cm³)
28	37	32	(28 + 37 + 32) ÷ 3 = 32	37 − 28 = 9

Ignore outliers when calculating the mean and range.

If Your Data Comes in Categories, Present It in a Bar Chart

You should be able to draw charts and plot graphs from results in a table.

1) Once you've recorded and processed your results, you should <u>present</u> them in a nice <u>chart</u> or <u>graph</u> to help you <u>spot any patterns</u> in your data.

2) If the independent variable is <u>categoric</u> (comes in distinct categories, e.g. blood group) or <u>discrete</u> (the data can be counted in chunks where there's no in-between value, e.g. number of bacteria) use a <u>bar chart</u> to display the data. Here are the <u>rules</u> for <u>drawing</u> bar charts:

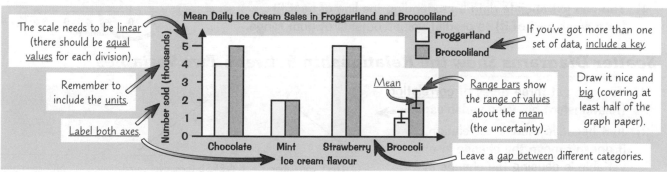

If Your Data is Continuous, Plot a Graph

If both variables are <u>continuous</u> (numerical data that can have any value within a range, e.g. length, volume, temperature), you should use a <u>graph</u> to display the data. Here are the rules for plotting points on a graph:

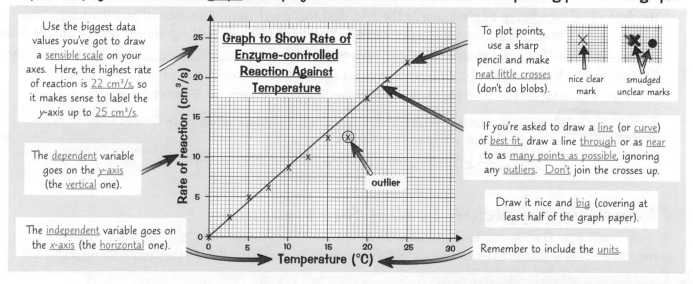

Chapter B7 — Ideas About Science

Processing and Presenting Data

Graphs Can Give You a Lot of Information About Your Data

1) The gradient (slope) of a graph tells you how quickly the dependent variable changes if you change the independent variable.

$$\text{gradient} = \frac{\text{change in } y}{\text{change in } x}$$

You can use this method to calculate any rates from a graph, not just the rate of a reaction. Just remember that a rate is how much something changes over time, so x needs to be the time.

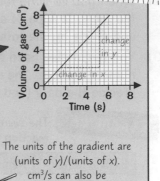

This graph shows the volume of gas produced in a reaction against time. The graph is linear (it's a straight line graph), so you can simply calculate the gradient of the line to find out the rate of reaction.

1) To calculate the gradient, pick two points on the line that are easy to read and a good distance apart.

2) Draw a line down from one of the points and a line across from the other to make a triangle. The line drawn down the side of the triangle is the change in y and the line across the bottom is the change in x.

Change in y = 6.8 – 2.0 = 4.8 cm³   Change in x = 5.2 – 1.6 = 3.6 s

$$\text{Rate} = \text{gradient} = \frac{\text{change in } y}{\text{change in } x} = \frac{4.8 \text{ cm}^3}{3.6 \text{ s}} = \underline{1.3 \text{ cm}^3/\text{s}} \text{ or } \underline{1.3 \text{ cm}^3\text{s}^{-1}}$$

The units of the gradient are (units of y)/(units of x). cm³/s can also be written as cm³s⁻¹.

2) The intercept of a graph is where the line of best fit crosses one of the axes. The x-intercept is where the line of best fit crosses the x-axis and the y-intercept is where it crosses the y-axis.

3) You can use the line of best fit to interpolate data — this means you can find approximate values in between the values you recorded. E.g. if you recorded the volume of gas produced at 2 second intervals and you wanted to work out how much was produced after 3 seconds, you could use your graph to work it out.

Read off the x-axis at the value you want to know until you reach the line of best fit.

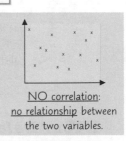

Then read across to find the corresponding value on the y-axis.

4) You can extrapolate data by extending the line of best fit (or a small part of it) to predict values outside of your range.

Scatter Diagrams Show the Relationship Between Two Variables

1) You can get three types of correlation (relationship) between variables:

2) Just because there's correlation, it doesn't mean the change in one variable is causing the change in the other — there might be other factors involved (see page 107).

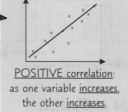

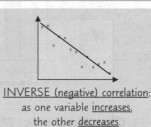

POSITIVE correlation: as one variable increases, the other increases.

INVERSE (negative) correlation: as one variable increases, the other decreases.

NO correlation: no relationship between the two variables.

When Doing a Calculation, Round to the Lowest Number of Significant Figures

The first significant figure of a number is the first digit that's not zero. The second and third significant figures come straight after (even if they're zeros). You should be aware of significant figures in calculations.

1) In any calculation, you should round the answer to the lowest number of significant figures (s.f.) given.

2) Remember to write down how many significant figures you've rounded to after your answer.

3) If your calculation has multiple steps, only round the final answer, or it won't be as accurate.

 **EXAMPLE:** A plant produces 10.2 cm³ of oxygen in 6.5 minutes whilst photosynthesising. Calculate the rate of photosynthesis.

rate = 10.2 cm³ ÷ 6.5 min = 1.5692... = 1.6 cm³/min (2 s.f.) —— Final answer should be rounded to 2 s.f.

10.2 — 3 s.f.   6.5 — 2 s.f.

I love eating apples — I call it core elation...

Science is all about finding relationships between things. And I don't mean that chemists gather together in corners to discuss whether or not Devini and Sebastian might be a couple... though they probably do that too.

Units and Equations

Graphs and maths skills are all very well, but the numbers don't mean much if you can't get the <u>units</u> right.

S.I. Units Are Used All Round the World

1) It wouldn't be all that useful if I defined volume in terms of <u>bath tubs</u>, you defined it in terms of <u>egg-cups</u> and my pal Sarwat defined it in terms of <u>balloons</u> — we'd never be able to compare our data.

2) To stop this happening, scientists have come up with a set of <u>standard units</u>, called S.I. units, that all scientists use to measure their data. Here are some S.I. units you might see in biology:

Quantity	S.I. Base Unit
mass	kilogram, kg
length	metre, m
time	second, s
amount of substance	mole, mol
temperature	kelvin, K

Scaling Prefixes Can Be Used for Large and Small Quantities

1) Quantities come in a huge <u>range</u> of sizes. For example, the volume of a swimming pool might be around 2 000 000 000 cm³, while the volume of a cup is around 250 cm³.

2) To make the size of numbers more <u>manageable</u>, larger or smaller units are used. These are the <u>S.I. base unit</u> (e.g. metres) with a <u>prefix</u> in front:

prefix	tera (T)	giga (G)	mega (M)	kilo (k)	deci (d)	centi (c)	milli (m)	micro (μ)	nano (n)
multiple of unit	10^{12}	10^9	1 000 000 (10^6)	1000	0.1	0.01	0.001	0.000001 (10^{-6})	10^{-9}

3) These <u>prefixes</u> tell you <u>how much bigger</u> or <u>smaller</u> a unit is than the base unit. So one <u>kilometre</u> is <u>one thousand</u> metres.

The conversion factor is the number of times the smaller unit goes into the larger unit.

4) To <u>swap</u> from one unit to another, all you need to know is what number you have to divide or multiply by to get from the original unit to the new unit — this is called the <u>conversion factor</u>.

- To go from a <u>bigger unit</u> (like m) to a <u>smaller unit</u> (like cm), you <u>multiply</u> by the conversion factor.
- To go from a <u>smaller unit</u> (like g) to a <u>bigger unit</u> (like kg), you <u>divide</u> by the conversion factor.

5) Here are some conversions that'll be useful for GCSE biology:

Mass can have units of kg and g.

kg ⟷ g (× 1000 / ÷ 1000)

Length can have lots of units, including mm, μm and nm.

mm ⟷ μm ⟷ nm (× 1000 / ÷ 1000)

Time can have units of min and s.

min ⟷ s (× 60 / ÷ 60)

Volume can have units of m³, dm³ and cm³.

m³ ⟷ dm³ ⟷ cm³ (× 1000 / ÷ 1000)

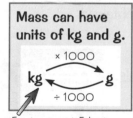

E.g. to convert 5 kg to g, multiply 5 by 1000 = 5000 g.

Always Check That The Values Used in Equations Have the Right Units

1) Formulas and equations show <u>relationships</u> between <u>variables</u>.

2) To <u>rearrange</u> an equation, make sure that whatever you do to <u>one side</u> of the equation, you also do to the <u>other side</u>.

You can find the <u>magnification</u> of something using the equation: magnification = measured size ÷ actual size (see p.61). You can <u>rearrange</u> this equation to find the <u>measured size</u> by <u>multiplying each side</u> by the actual size: measured size = magnification × actual size.

3) To use a formula, you need to know the values of <u>all but one</u> of the variables. <u>Substitute</u> the values you do know into the formula, and do the calculation to work out the final variable.

4) Always make sure the values you put into an equation or formula have the <u>right units</u>. For example, if you're calculating the magnification of something, but your image size is in mm and the real size is in μm, you'll have to <u>convert</u> both measurements into the same unit (either mm or μm) before you start.

5) To make sure your units are <u>correct</u>, it can help to write down the <u>units</u> on each line of your <u>calculation</u>.

I wasn't sure I liked units, but now I'm converted...

It's easy to get in a muddle when converting between units, but there's a handy way to check you've done it right. If you're moving from a smaller unit to a larger unit (e.g. g to kg) the number should get smaller, and vice versa.

Uncertainties and Evaluations

You can never be certain that your data is 100% correct. You need to decide how confident you are in it...

Uncertainty is the Amount of Error Your Measurements Might Have

1) When you repeat a measurement, you often get a slightly different figure each time you do it due to random error. This means that each result has some uncertainty to it.

2) The measurements you make will also have some uncertainty in them due to limits in the resolution of the equipment you use and human errors (see p. 102).

The range is the largest value minus the smallest value (p.103).

3) This all means that the mean of a set of results will also have some uncertainty to it. You can calculate the uncertainty of a mean result using the equation:

$$\text{uncertainty} = \frac{\text{range}}{2}$$

4) The larger the range, the less precise your results are and the more uncertainty there will be in your results. Uncertainties are shown using the '±' symbol.

The table below shows the results of a respiration experiment to determine the volume of carbon dioxide produced. Calculate the uncertainty of the mean.

Repeat	1	2	3	mean
Volume of CO_2 produced (cm^3)	20.2	19.8	20.0	20.0

1) First work out the range:
Range = 20.2 − 19.8
= 0.4 cm^3

2) Use the range to find the uncertainty:
Uncertainty = range ÷ 2 = 0.4 ÷ 2 = 0.2 cm^3.   So the uncertainty of the mean = 20.0 ± 0.2 cm^3

5) Measuring a greater amount of something helps to reduce uncertainty. For example, in a rate of reaction experiment, measuring the amount of product formed over a longer period compared to a shorter period will reduce the percentage uncertainty in your results.

You Need to Evaluate Your Data

Before you make any conclusions based on your data, you need to perform an evaluation.
An evaluation is a critical analysis of the whole investigation, including the data you obtained.

1) You should comment on the method — was it valid?
Did you control all the other variables to make it a fair test?

2) Comment on the quality of the results — were the results repeatable, reproducible, accurate and precise? Were there sources of random or systematic error?

3) Were there any outliers? If there were none then say so. If there were any, try to explain them — were they caused by errors in measurement? You should comment on the level of uncertainty in your results too.

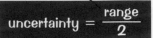

I'd value this E somewhere in the region of 250-300k.

4) All this analysis will allow you to say how confident you are that your results are good.

5) Then you can suggest any changes to the method that would improve the quality of the results, so that you could have more confidence in your data. For example, you might suggest changing the way you controlled a variable, carrying out further repeats or increasing the number of measurements you took. Taking more measurements at narrower intervals could give you a more accurate result. For example:

Enzymes have an optimum temperature (a temperature at which they work best). Say you do an experiment to find an enzyme's optimum temperature and take measurements at 10 °C, 20 °C, 30 °C, 40 °C and 50 °C. The results of this experiment tell you the optimum is 40 °C. You could then repeat the experiment, taking more measurements around 40 °C to a get a more accurate value for the optimum.

When suggesting improvements to the investigation, always make sure that you say why you think this would make the results better.

Evaluation — next time, I'll make sure I don't burn the lab down...

By now you should have realised how important trustworthy evidence is (even more important than a good supply of spot cream). Evaluations are a good way to assess evidence and see how things can be improved in the future.

Drawing Conclusions

Congratulations — you're nearly at the end of a gruelling investigation. Time to <u>draw conclusions</u>.

You Can Only Conclude What the Data Shows and NO MORE

1) Drawing conclusions might seem pretty straightforward — you just <u>look at your data</u> and <u>say what pattern or relationship you see</u> between the dependent and independent variables.

> The table on the right shows the heights of pea plant seedlings grown for three weeks with <u>different fertilisers</u>.
>
> <u>CONCLUSION</u>: Fertiliser <u>B</u> makes <u>pea plant</u> seedlings grow taller over a <u>three week</u> period than fertiliser A.

Fertiliser	Mean growth / mm
A	13.5
B	19.5
No fertiliser	5.5

2) But you've got to be really careful that your conclusion <u>matches the data</u> you've got and <u>doesn't go any further</u>.

> You <u>can't</u> conclude that fertiliser B makes <u>any other type of plant</u> grow taller than fertiliser A — the results could be totally different.

3) You also need to be able to <u>use your results</u> to <u>justify your conclusion</u> (i.e. back up your conclusion with some specific data).

> Over the three week period, fertiliser B made the pea plants grow <u>6 mm more</u> on average than fertiliser A.

4) When writing a conclusion you need to <u>refer back</u> to the original hypothesis and say whether the data <u>supports it</u> or not. You might remember from page 99 that if data backs up a prediction, it <u>increases confidence</u> in the hypothesis (although it doesn't prove the hypothesis is correct). If the data doesn't support the prediction, it can <u>decrease confidence</u> in it.

> The <u>hypothesis</u> for this experiment might have been that adding fertiliser would <u>increase the growth</u> of plants because it would provide plants with <u>nutrients</u>. The <u>prediction</u> may have been that <u>fertiliser B</u> contained more nutrients and so would <u>increase growth more</u> than fertiliser A. If so, the data <u>increases confidence</u> in the hypothesis.

5) You could also make more <u>predictions</u> based on your conclusion, then <u>further experiments</u> could be carried out to test them.

Don't Forget, Correlation DOES NOT Mean Cause

Scientists often find <u>correlations</u> between variables by spotting <u>patterns</u> in data. However, just because there's a <u>correlation</u> (relationship) between a factor and an outcome, it <u>doesn't mean</u> that the factor <u>causes</u> the outcome. There are several reasons for this...

1) Sometimes two things can show a correlation purely due to <u>chance</u>. This is why an <u>individual case</u> (e.g. a correlation between people's hair colour and how good they are at frisbee in a particular school) <u>isn't enough</u> to <u>convince scientists</u> that a factor is causing an outcome. <u>Repeatable</u>, <u>reproducible</u> data must be collected first.

2) A lot of the time it may look as if a factor is causing an outcome but it isn't — <u>another</u>, hidden <u>factor</u> links them both. For example:

> There's a correlation between <u>water temperature</u> and <u>shark attacks</u>. This isn't because warmer water makes sharks crazy. Instead, they're linked by a third variable — the <u>number of people swimming</u> (more people swim when the water's hotter, and with more people in the water you get more shark attacks).

3) Sometimes a correlation is just when a factor makes an outcome <u>more likely</u>, but <u>not inevitable</u>. E.g. if you eat a diet high in saturated fat, it increases your risk of heart disease, but it doesn't mean you will get it. That's because there are <u>lots of different factors interacting</u> to influence the outcome.

4) Scientists don't usually accept that a factor causes an outcome (there is a <u>cause-effect link</u>) unless they can work out a <u>plausible mechanism</u> that <u>links</u> the <u>two things</u>.

> For example, there's a correlation between <u>smoking</u> and <u>lung cancer</u>. Cigarette smoke contains cancer-causing chemicals and it's inhaled into the lungs — this is the mechanism.

I conclude that this page is a bit dull...

...although, just because I find it dull doesn't mean that I can conclude it's dull. In the exam you could be given a conclusion and asked whether the data supports it — you need to make sure the data fully justifies the conclusion.

New Technologies and Risk

By reading this page you are agreeing to the risk of a paper cut or severe drowsiness...

Scientific Technology Usually Has Benefits and Negative Impacts

Scientists have created loads of new technologies that could improve our lives.
In genetics, for example, benefits include:

- Being able to identify whether a fetus has a genetic disorder.
- Identifying whether an adult is likely to get a disease, such as cancer, later in life.
- The possibility of being able to cure some genetic disorders.
- Genetically engineering plants with useful characteristics, e.g. insect resistance in crops.

However, it's not all good news. Sometimes new technology can have unintended or undesired impacts on our quality of life or the environment. For example:

Altering someone's genes to cure a genetic disorder might affect their health in other ways — there's no way of knowing in advance. This could reduce their overall quality of life.

When developing new technologies, scientists try to come up with ways to reduce these risks, but...

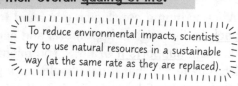
To reduce environmental impacts, scientists try to use natural resources in a sustainable way (at the same rate as they are replaced).

Nothing is Completely Risk-Free

1) Everything we do has a risk attached to it — this is the chance that it will cause harm.

2) The risks of some things seem pretty obvious, or we've known about them for a while, like the risk of causing acid rain by polluting the atmosphere, or of having a car accident when you're travelling in a car.

3) New technology arising from scientific advances can bring new risks, e.g. scientists are unsure whether nanoparticles that are being used in cosmetics and suncream might be harming the cells in our bodies. These risks need to be considered alongside the benefits of the technology, e.g. improved sun protection.

4) You can estimate the size of a risk based on how many times something happens in a big sample (e.g. 100 000 people) over a given period (e.g. a year). For example, you could assess the risk of a driver crashing by recording how many people in a group of 100 000 drivers crashed their cars over a year.

5) To make decisions about activities that involve hazards, we need to take into account the chance of the hazard causing harm, and how serious the consequences would be if it did. If an activity involves a hazard that's very likely to cause harm, with serious consequences if it does, it's considered high risk.

People Make Their Own Decisions About Risk

1) Not all risks have the same consequences, e.g. if you chop veg with a sharp knife you risk cutting your finger, but if you go scuba-diving you risk death. You're much more likely to cut your finger during half an hour of chopping than to die during half an hour of scuba-diving. But most people are happier to accept a higher probability of an accident if the consequences are short-lived and fairly minor.

2) People tend to be more willing to accept a risk if they choose to do something (e.g. go scuba diving), compared to having the risk imposed on them (e.g. having a nuclear power station built next door).

3) People's perception of risk (how risky they think something is) isn't always accurate. There is sometimes a big difference between perceived risk and calculated risk. People tend to view familiar activities as low-risk and unfamiliar activities as high-risk — even if that's not the case. For example, cycling on roads is often high-risk, but many people are happy to do it because it's a familiar activity. Air travel is actually pretty safe, but a lot of people perceive it as high-risk. People also over-estimate unfamiliar things that have long-term or invisible effects, e.g. ionising radiation.

Not revising — an unacceptable exam risk...

All activities pose some sort of risk, it's just a question of deciding whether that risk is worth it in the long run.

Communication and Issues Created by Science

Scientific developments can be great, but they can sometimes <u>raise more questions</u> than they answer...

It's Important to Communicate Scientific Discoveries

1) Scientists need to be able to <u>communicate their findings</u> to <u>other scientists</u>, and groups like the <u>public</u> and <u>politicians</u>, so that <u>decisions</u> can be <u>made</u>. For example:

> Gene technology is used in <u>genetic engineering</u> to produce <u>genetically modified crops</u>. Information about these crops needs to be communicated to <u>politicians</u> who <u>pass laws</u> about growing them and to the <u>general public</u>, so they can make <u>informed decisions</u> about the food they buy and eat.

2) One way discoveries can be communicated to the public is through the <u>media</u>. However, <u>reports</u> about scientific discoveries in the <u>media</u> (e.g. newspapers or television) <u>aren't</u> peer-reviewed.

3) This means that, even though news stories are often <u>based</u> on data that has been peer-reviewed, the data might be <u>presented</u> in a way that is <u>over-simplified</u> or <u>inaccurate</u>, making it open to <u>misinterpretation</u>.

4) People who want to make a point can sometimes <u>present data</u> in a <u>biased way</u>. (Sometimes <u>without knowing</u> they're doing it.) For example, a scientist might overemphasise a relationship in the data, or a newspaper article might describe details of data <u>supporting</u> an idea without giving any evidence <u>against</u> it.

Scientific Developments are Great, but they can Raise Issues

Scientific <u>knowledge is increased</u> by doing experiments. And this knowledge leads to <u>scientific developments</u>, e.g. new technologies or new advice. These developments can create <u>issues</u> though. For example:

<u>Economic issues:</u> Society <u>can't</u> always <u>afford</u> to do things scientists recommend (e.g. investing in alternative energy sources) without <u>cutting back elsewhere</u>.

<u>Environmental issues:</u> <u>Human activity</u> often affects the <u>natural environment</u> — e.g. <u>genetically modified crops</u> may help us to produce <u>more food</u> — but some people think they could cause <u>environmental problems</u> (see p.11).

<u>Social issues:</u> Decisions based on scientific evidence affect <u>people</u>. E.g. should <u>alcohol</u> be <u>banned</u> to <u>prevent health problems</u>?

<u>Personal issues:</u> Some decisions will affect <u>individuals</u>. People can even have different views in different contexts. For example, someone might support <u>alternative energy</u>, but object if a <u>wind farm</u> is built next to their house.

Science Can't Answer Every Question — Especially Ethical Ones

1) In order to answer scientific questions, scientists need <u>data</u> to provide <u>evidence</u> for their hypotheses.

2) Some questions can't be answered <u>yet</u> because the data <u>can't</u> currently be <u>collected</u>, or because there's <u>not enough</u> data to <u>support</u> a theory. <u>Eventually</u>, as we get <u>more evidence</u>, we'll answer some of the questions that <u>currently</u> can't be answered, e.g. what the impact of global warming on sea levels will be.

3) But there will always be the "<u>Should we be doing this at all?</u>"-type questions that experiments <u>can't</u> help us to answer...

> Think about <u>new drugs which can be taken to boost your 'brain power'</u>.
> - Some people think they're <u>good</u> as they could improve concentration or memory. New drugs could let people think in ways beyond the powers of normal brains.
> - Other people say they're <u>bad</u> — they could give you an <u>unfair advantage</u> in exams. And people might be <u>pressured</u> into taking them so that they could work more <u>effectively</u>, and for <u>longer hours</u>.

> THE GAZETTE
> BRAIN-BOOSTING DRUGS MAKE A MOCKERY OF EXAMS
>
> THE POST
> GENIUS PILLS TO BECOME THE NEW COFFEE

4) When making decisions that involve <u>ethical dilemmas</u> like this, a commonly used argument is that the <u>right decision</u> is the one that brings the <u>greatest benefit</u> to the <u>most people</u>.

Tea to milk or milk to tea? — Totally unanswerable by science...

Science can't tell you whether or not you should do something. That's for you and society to decide. But there are tons of questions science might be able to answer, like where life came from and where my superhero socks are.

Revision Questions for Chapter B7

Well, that wraps up <u>Chapter B7</u> — there's a lot of scientific know-how on these pages, so give yourself a test.

- Try these questions and <u>tick off each one</u> when you <u>get it right</u>.
- When you've done <u>all the questions</u> for a topic and are <u>completely happy</u> with it, tick off the topic.

The Scientific Method (p.98-99) ☑

1) What is a hypothesis? ☑
2) Give two reasons why scientists may come up with different explanations for the same observation. ☑
3) How does new technology change the way we can test explanations? ☑
4) Briefly explain how the peer-review process works. ☑
5) True or false? "Scientific theories are explanations that still need to be accepted." ☑
6) Give an example of a model and explain how it can be used to make predictions. ☑

Designing Investigations and Collecting Data (p.100-102) ☑

7) How could a scientist try to make their investigation a fair test? ☑
8) Give one way in which you could control the temperature of a beaker during an investigation. ☑
9) Why is a control experiment important in an investigation? ☑
10) Give two potential hazards in an experiment and explain what you would do to reduce the risk. ☑
11) Give one reason why it is better to have a large sample size than a small sample size in an investigation. ☑
12) Suggest how you would work out the range of variable values to use in your experiment. ☑
13) What are precise results? ☑
14) What type of error is caused if a measurement is wrong by the same amount every time? ☑

Processing and Presenting Data, Units and Equations (p.104-105) ☑

15) How would you calculate: a) the mean of a set of results, b) the range of results? ☑
16) Sally does a survey to find the number of different types of mollusc on a beach.
   Should she present her findings in a bar chart or a graph? Why? ☑
17) What is the intercept of a graph? ☑
18) Sketch a graph showing: a) a positive correlation, b) a negative correlation. ☑
19) Which of the following prefixes signifies a smaller unit: nano or micro? ☑
20) How would you convert from grams to kilograms? ☑

Uncertainties, Evaluations and Conclusions (p.106-107) ☑

21) How can you calculate the uncertainty of a mean result? ☑
22) Give four things you should consider when evaluating data. ☑
23) Describe the effect data has on the hypothesis if the data backs up the prediction. ☑
24) What do scientists need to find to accept a cause-effect link between a factor and an outcome? ☑

New Technologies and Risk (p.108) ☑

25) How might someone calculate risk? ☑
26) True or false? "People are more likely to perceive an unfamiliar situation as high-risk." ☑

Communication and Issues Created by Science (p.109) ☑

27) Why is it important that scientists communicate their findings to the public? ☑
28) Give one common argument about the best way to make decisions involving ethical dilemmas. ☑

Safety, Ethics and Sampling

- You're expected to carry out a minimum of <u>8 practical activities</u> as part of your course. Your teacher will pick which ones you do, but examples of suitable activities are covered in <u>Chapters B1-B6</u> of this book. They're highlighted with <u>practical stamps</u> like this one.

- The practicals marked with a stamp also cover a whole load of <u>practical skills</u>, which you need to learn for your exams.

- This chapter covers some <u>extra bits and bobs</u> you need to know about practical work.

PRACTICAL

At least 15% of the marks in your exams will be for questions that test practical skills.

Make Sure You're Working Safely in the Lab

1) <u>Before</u> you start any experiment, make sure you know about any <u>safety precautions</u> to do with your <u>method</u> or the <u>chemicals</u> you're using. You need to <u>follow</u> any instructions that your teacher gives you <u>carefully</u>. The chemicals you're using may be <u>hazardous</u> — for example, they might be <u>flammable</u> (<u>catch fire easily</u>), or they might <u>irritate</u> or <u>burn</u> your <u>skin</u> if it comes into contact with them.

2) Make sure that you're wearing <u>sensible clothing</u> when you're in the lab (e.g. open shoes won't protect your feet from spillages). When you're doing an experiment, you should wear a <u>lab coat</u> to protect your skin and clothing. Depending on the experiment, you may need to also wear <u>safety goggles</u> and <u>gloves</u>.

3) You also need to be aware of <u>general safety</u> in the lab, e.g. keep anything <u>flammable</u> away from lit Bunsen burners, don't directly touch any <u>hot equipment</u>, handle <u>glassware</u> carefully so it doesn't <u>break</u>, etc.

You Need to Think About Ethical Issues In Your Experiments

1) Any <u>organisms</u> involved in your investigations need to be treated <u>safely</u> and <u>ethically</u>.

2) <u>Animals</u> need to be treated <u>humanely</u> — they should be <u>handled carefully</u> and any wild animals captured for studying (e.g. during an investigation of the distribution of an organism) should be <u>returned to their original habitat</u>. Any animals kept in the lab should also be <u>cared for</u> in a humane way, e.g. the <u>conditions</u> that they are kept in shouldn't <u>harm</u> or <u>kill</u> them.

3) If you're carrying out an experiment involving other <u>students</u> (e.g. investigating pulse rate), they should not be forced to participate <u>against their will</u> or feel <u>pressured</u> to take part.

Organisms Should Be Sampled At Random Sites in an Area

1) It's generally <u>not possible</u> to count <u>every single organism</u> in an area. So if you're interested in the <u>distribution</u> of an organism in an area, or its <u>population size</u>, you need to take <u>samples</u> of the population in the area you're interested in.

2) You can use <u>quadrats</u> or <u>transects</u> to take population samples — see pages 45-46.

3) If you only take samples from <u>one part</u> of an area, your results will be <u>biased</u> — they may not give an <u>accurate representation</u> of the <u>whole area</u>.

4) To make sure that your sampling isn't biased, it needs to be <u>random</u>. This means you need to use a method of <u>choosing sampling sites</u> in which every site has an <u>equal chance</u> of being chosen. E.g.

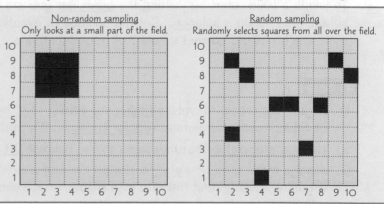

If you're looking at plant species in a field...

1) <u>Divide</u> the field into a <u>grid</u>.

2) <u>Label the grid</u> along the bottom and up the side with numbers or letters.

3) Use a <u>random number generator</u> (e.g. on a computer or calculator) to select coordinates, e.g. 2,4; 7,3.

4) Take your samples at these coordinates.

Non-random sampling
Only looks at a small part of the field.

Random sampling
Randomly selects squares from all over the field.

There's a single birch in my garden — it's a random sapling...

Have a good think about safety, ethics and bias before you start any experimental work — it's all important stuff.

Measuring Substances

Get your lab coats on, it's time to find out about the skills you'll need in <u>experiments</u>...

Use the Right Apparatus to Take Accurate Readings

1) Length

1) <u>Length</u> can be <u>measured</u> in different <u>units</u> (e.g. mm, cm, m). Smaller units have a higher degree of <u>accuracy</u>. For example, it's more <u>accurate</u> to measure the length of a potato cylinder to the nearest <u>mm</u> than the nearest <u>cm</u>.

2) You'll need to decide on the <u>appropriate level of accuracy</u> for your experiment. For example, the length of a <u>leaf</u> would be better measured in <u>millimetres</u>, but the length of a <u>transect line</u> would be better measured in <u>metres</u>.

3) It is also important to <u>choose</u> the <u>right equipment</u> when measuring length — a <u>ruler</u> would probably be best for small things, but a <u>metre rule</u> or <u>tape measure</u> would be better for larger distances.

How big?

2) Area

In biology, you might need to measure the <u>area</u> of something (e.g. part of a habitat, a living thing). Living things are usually quite <u>complex shapes</u>, but you can make their area easier to work out by comparing them to a <u>simpler shape</u> and working out the area of that (e.g. <u>clear zones</u> in bacterial lawns are roughly <u>circular</u> — see p.20-21). To find the area of something:

1) First, you'll need to take <u>accurate measurements</u> of its dimensions.

> If you want to <u>measure</u> the area of a <u>field</u> (see page 45) that is <u>rectangular</u>, you'll need to use a <u>tape measure</u> or a <u>trundle wheel</u> to measure the <u>length</u> and <u>width</u> of the field. Record your readings in metres.

2) Then you can <u>calculate</u> its <u>area</u>.

> Area of a <u>rectangle</u> = <u>length</u> × <u>width</u>.
> So, if your field is 30 m by 55 m, the <u>area</u> would be 30 × 55 = <u>1650 m²</u>.

Don't forget that units of area are always something squared, e.g. mm².

Here are some examples of other area formulas that may come in useful:

- Area of a triangle = ½ × base × height
- Area of a circle = πr^2

3) Mass

To weigh a solid, start by putting the <u>container</u> you are weighing your substance into on a <u>balance</u>. Set the balance to exactly <u>zero</u> and then weigh out the correct amount of your substance. Easy peasy.

4) Time

1) If your experiment involves <u>timing</u> something (e.g. how long a reaction takes to happen) or taking measurements at <u>regular intervals</u>, it's probably best to use a <u>stopwatch</u>.

2) Using a <u>stopwatch</u> that measures to the nearest <u>0.1 s</u> will make your results more <u>accurate</u>.

3) Always make sure you <u>start</u> and <u>stop</u> the stopwatch at exactly the right time. For example, if you're investigating the rate of a reaction, you should start timing at the <u>exact moment</u> you mix the reagents and start the reaction.

4) It's a good idea to get the <u>same person</u> to do the timing so the results are as <u>precise</u> as possible.

Measuring Substances

5) Temperature

You can use a <u>thermometer</u> to measure temperature. Make sure that the <u>bulb</u> of the thermometer is <u>completely submerged</u> in the substance you're measuring and that you wait for the temperature to <u>stabilise</u> before you take your initial reading. Read off the <u>scale</u> on the thermometer at <u>eye level</u> to make sure your reading is correct.

When you're reading off a scale, write down the value of the graduation that the amount is closest to. If it's exactly halfway between two values, round up.

6) Volume of a Liquid

There's more than one way to measure the volume of a <u>liquid</u>. Whichever method you use, always read the volume from the <u>bottom of the meniscus</u> (the curved upper surface of the liquid) when it's at <u>eye level</u>.

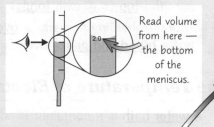

Read volume from here — the bottom of the meniscus.

*   <u>Using a pipette</u> — <u>Pipettes</u> are used to suck up and <u>transfer</u> volumes of liquid between containers. <u>Dropping pipettes</u> are used to transfer <u>drops</u> of liquid. <u>Graduated pipettes</u> are used to transfer <u>accurate</u> volumes. A <u>pipette filler</u> is attached to the end of a graduated pipette, to <u>control</u> the amount of liquid being drawn up.

*   <u>Using a measuring cylinder</u> — <u>Measuring cylinders</u> come in all different <u>sizes</u>. Make sure you choose one that's the right size for the measurement you want to make. It's no good using a huge 1 dm³ cylinder to measure out 2 cm³ of a liquid — the graduations will be too big, and you'll end up with <u>massive errors</u>. It'd be much better to use one that measures up to 10 cm³.

7) Volume of a Gas

1) To accurately measure the <u>volume</u> of gas, you should use a <u>gas syringe</u>.

2) Alternatively, you can use an <u>upturned measuring cylinder</u> filled with <u>water</u>. The gas will <u>displace</u> the water so you can <u>read the volume</u> off the <u>scale</u> — this method is shown on page 33.

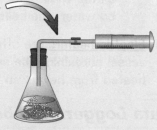

3) You could also <u>count the bubbles</u> of gas released. But the bubbles released could be <u>different sizes</u> and if they're produced quickly, you might <u>miss some</u>. So this method is <u>less accurate</u>.

4) When you're measuring a gas, you need to make sure that the equipment is set up so that none of the gas can <u>escape</u>, otherwise your results won't be <u>accurate</u>.

8) pH

The method you should use to measure pH depends on what your experiment is.

1) <u>Indicators</u> are dyes that <u>change colour</u> depending on whether they're in an <u>acid</u> or an <u>alkali</u>. You use them by adding a couple of drops of the indicator to the solution you're interested in. <u>Universal indicator</u> is a <u>mixture</u> of indicators that changes colour <u>gradually</u> as pH changes. It's useful for <u>estimating</u> the pH of a solution based on its colour.

2) <u>Indicator paper</u> is useful if you don't want to colour the entire solution that you're testing. It <u>changes colour</u> depending on the pH of the solution it touches. You can also hold a piece of <u>damp indicator paper</u> in a <u>gas sample</u> to test its pH.

Blue litmus paper turns <u>red</u> in acidic conditions and red litmus paper turns <u>blue</u> in alkaline conditions.

3) <u>pH meters</u> have a <u>digital display</u> that gives an <u>accurate value</u> for the pH of a solution.

Experimentus apparatus...

Wizardry won't help you here, unfortunately. It's best you just get your head down and learn this stuff.

Heating Substances & Continuous Sampling

You can use <u>technology</u> to make your life a bit easier in the lab — but first, the good ole' <u>Bunsen burner</u>...

Bunsen Burners Have a Naked Flame

Bunsen burners are good for <u>heating things quickly</u>. But you need to make sure you're using them <u>safely</u>:

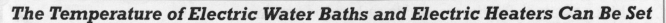

- You should always use a Bunsen burner on a <u>heat-proof mat</u>.
- If your Bunsen burner is alight but not heating anything, make sure you <u>close</u> the hole so that the flame becomes <u>yellow</u> and <u>clearly visible</u>.
- Use the <u>blue</u> flame to heat things. If you're heating a vessel <u>in</u> the flame, hold it at the <u>top</u> (e.g. with <u>tongs</u>) and point the opening <u>away from</u> yourself (and others).
- If you're heating something <u>over</u> the flame (e.g. a beaker of water), you should put a <u>tripod and gauze</u> over the Bunsen burner before you light it, and place the vessel on this.

Heat-proof mat
Hole is closed
gas

The Temperature of Electric Water Baths and Electric Heaters Can Be Set

1) A <u>water bath</u> is a container filled with water that can be heated to a <u>specific temperature</u>. A <u>simple</u> water bath can be made by heating a <u>beaker of water</u> over a <u>Bunsen burner</u> and monitoring the temperature with a <u>thermometer</u>. However, it is difficult to keep the temperature of the water <u>constant</u>.

2) A <u>thermostatically controlled water bath</u> will <u>monitor</u> and <u>adjust</u> the temperature. Here's how to use one:

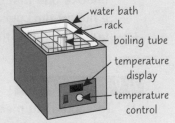

- <u>Set</u> the temperature on the water bath, and allow the water to <u>heat up</u>.
- Place the boiling tube containing your substance in the water bath using <u>test tube holders</u>. The level of the water outside the boiling tube should be <u>just above</u> the level of the substance inside the boiling tube.
- The substance will then be warmed to the <u>same temperature</u> as the water. As the substance in the boiling tube is surrounded by water, the heating is very <u>even</u>.

water bath
rack
boiling tube
temperature display
temperature control

3) <u>Electric heaters</u> are often made up of a metal plate that can be heated to a specified temperature. The vessel containing the substance you want to heat is placed on top of the hot plate. The vessel is only heated from below, so you'll usually have to <u>stir</u> the substance inside to make sure it's <u>heated evenly</u>.

Data Loggers can be Used to Take Continuous Samples

1) <u>Continuous sampling</u> is when <u>lots of samples</u> are taken at <u>regular intervals</u> over a particular time period.

2) Taking lots of samples means you can see what is happening <u>during the experiment</u>, not just the outcome of it.

3) Using a <u>data logger</u> connected to a computer is an <u>example</u> of continuous sampling. If you're going to use a data logger in one of your experiments, you'll need to:

- Decide <u>what</u> you are <u>measuring</u> and <u>what type</u> of <u>data logger</u> you will need, e.g. temperature, pH.
- Connect an <u>external sensor</u> to the data logger if you need to.
- Decide <u>how often</u> you want the data logger to take readings depending on the <u>length of the process</u> that you are measuring.

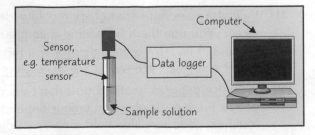

Computer
Sensor, e.g. temperature sensor
Data logger
Sample solution

4) You can use the computer to <u>view the data</u> and to <u>process</u> it (draw graphs, calculate averages, etc.).

5) Using a data logger to take measurements can improve the <u>accuracy</u> of your results because you can take a <u>large sample size</u>.

Electric water bath, lots of bubbles and a good book — suits me...

Ah, Bunsen burners — always make me feel like a real scientist. You've got to be on guard when there's fire about though. Using electric water baths or hot plates can be a safer way to go — but there's still the potential for scalds.

Answers

Page 2 — Cells and Genetic Material
Q1 As one long circular chromosome *[1 mark]* or in a plasmid *[1 mark]*.

Page 3 — Cells and Microscopes
Q1 Select the lowest-powered objective lens *[1 mark]* and move the stage up so the slide is just underneath the objective lens *[1 mark]*. Looking through the lens, move the stage downwards until the specimen is nearly in focus *[1 mark]*. Adjust the height of the stage with the fine adjustment knob until the image is in focus *[1 mark]*.

Page 4 — Genomes and Characteristics
Q1 The entire genetic material of an organism *[1 mark]*.

Q2 a) An organism's genotype is the combination of alleles it has for each gene *[1 mark]*.

b) An organism's phenotype is the characteristics that it displays *[1 mark]*.

Page 5 — DNA and Protein Synthesis
Q1 Each triplet of bases in a gene codes for an amino acid *[1 mark]*. The order of triplets in a gene determines the order of amino acids in a protein *[1 mark]*.

Page 6 — Mutations and Genetic Variants
Q1 A gene mutation alters the base sequence of DNA in a gene *[1 mark]*, which may affect the order of amino acids in the protein produced *[1 mark]*. This may lead to changes in the structure and function of the protein, which may alter the phenotype *[1 mark]*.

Page 7 — Genetic Diagrams
Q1 E.g.

	T	t
T	TT	Tt
t	Tt	tt

Proportion of offspring expected to be dwarf plants = 1 in 4.
[1 mark for correctly identifying the parents' genotypes as Tt, 1 mark for a correct genetic diagram, 1 mark for correct proportion.]

Page 8 — More Genetic Diagrams
Q1 Ff and ff *[1 mark]*.

Page 9 — Mendel
Q1 Mendel crossed dwarf pea plants with tall pea plants *[1 mark]* and discovered that the height of the offspring was influenced by the height of the parents *[1 mark]*. This lead to the understanding that there were inherited factors that could control characteristics *[1 mark]*.

Page 10 — Genome Research and Testing
Q1 E.g. the amniotic fluid surrounding the fetus could be sampled *[1 mark]* to obtain fetal DNA, which could be tested for genetic variants linked to a disorder *[1 mark]*.

Page 11 — Genetic Engineering
Q1 It can improve the yield of the crop *[1 mark]*, because herbicide-resistant crops can be sprayed with herbicides to kill weeds without the crop being damaged *[1 mark]*.

Page 13 — Health and Disease
Q1 A disease which is not spread from one organism to another *[1 mark]*.

Page 14 — How Disease Spreads
Q1 Any three from: e.g. in water / by air / by contact with infected surfaces / in body fluids / by animal vectors / in soil / in food *[1 mark for each correct answer, up to 3 marks]*.

Page 15 — Defending Against Pathogens
Q1 E.g. leaves and stems have a waxy cuticle *[1 mark]*. Plant cells are surrounded by cell walls *[1 mark]*.

Page 16 — The Human Immune System
Q1 E.g. antibodies disable the pathogen / antibodies 'tag' the pathogens, which helps phagocytes to find them so that they can engulf them *[1 mark]*.

Q2 Memory cells remain in the blood after the first infection with a pathogen *[1 mark]*. If the same pathogen enters the body again, they trigger the rapid production of antibodies so that the pathogen doesn't cause disease *[1 mark]*.

Page 17 — Reducing and Preventing the Spread of Disease
Q1 Benefit: e.g. changing the type of plants that are grown stops the pathogens becoming established in an area since many pathogens are specific to a particular plant *[1 mark]*. Cost: e.g. it may limit how profitable a farm is if it has to change farming practices for a different crop each year *[1 mark]*.

Page 18 — Vaccinations
Q1 They produce antibodies *[1 mark]* that attack the antigens present on the cells within the vaccination *[1 mark]*.

Page 19 — Detecting Diseases
Q1 By adding a stain to the sample, only certain bacterial species will absorb the stain *[1 mark]*. When the sample is then viewed under a microscope, any stained bacteria can be more easily identified *[1 mark]*.

Page 21 — Culturing Microorganisms
Q1 a) A *[1 mark]*

b) diameter = 13 mm
radius = 13 ÷ 2 = 6.5 mm
$\pi r^2 = \pi \times 6.5^2$ *[1 mark]*
= 132.7... = 133 mm² *[1 mark]*

c) E.g. a disc soaked in sterile water *[1 mark]*.

d) To show that any difference in the growth of the bacteria is only due to the effect of the antibiotic *[1 mark]*.

Page 22 — Monoclonal Antibodies
Q1 Monoclonal antibodies are identical antibodies produced from the same type of white blood cell *[1 mark]*.

Page 23 — More on Monoclonal Antibodies
Q1 Anti-cancer drugs can be attached to monoclonal antibodies *[1 mark]* and injected into the patient's blood *[1 mark]*. The monoclonal antibodies bind to specific tumour markers on cancer cells and so deliver the drug to these cells *[1 mark]*.

Page 24 — Non-Communicable Diseases
Q1 E.g. eating too much *[1 mark]*, not exercising regularly *[1 mark]*.

Page 25 — More on Non-Communicable Diseases
Q1 E.g. increasing the price of cigarettes may mean that fewer people are able to afford them *[1 mark]*, which may lead to a decrease in the national prevalence of lung cancer *[1 mark]*.

Page 26 — Interpreting Data on Disease
Q1 A bigger sample size makes it more likely that more of the different characteristics present in the whole population will be included in the sample *[1 mark]*.

Page 27 — Investigating Pulse Rate
Q1 The time taken for the heart rate to return to its normal resting rate after exercise *[1 mark]*.

Page 28 — Treating Disease
Q1 Many antibiotics are being misused *[1 mark]*, which has caused antibiotic-resistant strains of bacteria to become more common *[1 mark]*. This means that many antibiotics are less effective at killing the bacteria that cause bacterial infections *[1 mark]*.

Page 29 — Treating Cardiovascular Disease
Q1 E.g. they can cause excessive bleeding if the person taking them is hurt in an accident *[1 mark]*.

Page 30 — Developing New Medicines
Q1 In a double-blind trial, patients are randomly put into two groups — some receive the drug and some receive a placebo *[1 mark]*. Neither the patient nor the doctor knows whether the patient is getting the drug or a placebo until all of the results have been gathered *[1 mark]*.

Page 32 — Enzymes
Q1 If the pH is too high or too low, it can interfere with the bonds holding the enzyme together *[1 mark]*. This changes the shape of the active site *[1 mark]* and denatures the enzyme *[1 mark]*.

Page 33 — More on Enzymes
Q1 33 ÷ 60 = 0.55 cm³/s *[1 mark]*.

Page 34 — Photosynthesis
Q1 Plants produce glucose during photosynthesis. Some of this glucose is stored as starch *[1 mark]*. If you perform the starch test on a leaf grown without light, the leaf will not turn blue-black *[1 mark]* this means that there is no starch present in the leaf *[1 mark]*. As no starch has been made in the leaf grown without light, it shows that light is needed for plants to photosynthesise *[1 mark]*.

Page 35 — Investigating the Rate of Photosynthesis
Q1 Plants release oxygen into the atmosphere when they photosynthesise *[1 mark]*, therefore the more a plant photosynthesises, the more oyxgen it produces *[1 mark]*.

Page 36 — Limiting Factors of Photosynthesis
Q1 The rate of photosynthesis increases with increasing light intensity/is directly proportional to light intensity *[1 mark]* up to a point at which the rate levels off *[1 mark]*.

Page 37 — Diffusion, Osmosis and Active Transport
Q1 E.g. active transport requires energy and diffusion is passive *[1 mark]*. Active transport moves substances against a concentration gradient whereas diffusion is the movement of substances down a concentration gradient *[1 mark]*.

Page 38 — Transport in Plants and Prokaryotes
Q1 Each branch of a plant's roots is covered in millions of root hair cells *[1 mark]*, which gives the plant a big surface area for absorbing water and mineral ions from the soil *[1 mark]*.

Page 39 — Investigating Diffusion and Osmosis
Q1 That it is also 0.3 mol/dm³ *[1 mark]*. If the cells are surrounded by a solution with the same concentration as the fluid inside them, then water will not move in or out of the cells by osmosis *[1 mark]* and the cylinders won't lose or gain mass *[1 mark]*.

Page 40 — Xylem and Phloem
Q1 Water evaporates and diffuses from a plant's surface, creating a slight shortage of water in the leaf *[1 mark]*. This draws more water up from the rest of the plant through the xylem vessels to replace it *[1 mark]*. This in turn means more water is drawn up from the roots *[1 mark]*.

Answers

Page 41 — Stomata
Q1 Potassium ions are pumped into guard cells in response to light *[1 mark]*. This increases the solute concentration of the guard cells (which decreases the concentration of water molecules) *[1 mark]*. Water then moves into the guard cells by osmosis *[1 mark]*. This makes the guard cells turgid and the stoma opens *[1 mark]*.

Page 42 — Transpiration Rate
Q1 percentage change $= \dfrac{217 - 262}{262} \times 100$
$= -17.2\%$ (to 3 s.f.)
[2 marks for correct answer, otherwise 1 mark for (217 - 262) / 262].

Page 43 — Using a Potometer
Q1 E.g. light intensity, air movement *[2 marks]*.

Page 44 — Ecosystems and Interactions Between Organisms
Q1 Any two from: e.g. temperature / moisture level / light intensity / pH of the soil / toxic chemicals. *[1 mark for each correct answer, up to 2 marks]*

Page 45 — Investigating Ecosystems
Q1 Population size = (number in first sample × number in second sample) ÷ number in second sample previously marked
= (22 × 26) ÷ 4 = 143 crabs
[2 marks for correct answer, otherwise 1 mark for correct working]

Page 46 — More on Investigating Ecosystems
Q1 Mark out a line in the area you want to study using a tape measure *[1 mark]*. Place quadrats at intervals/next to each other along the line *[1 mark]*. Count and record the organisms in each quadrat *[1 mark]*.

Page 47 — Investigating Factors Affecting Distribution
Q1 The presence of bushy lichen indicates the air is clean *[1 mark]* because the lichen needs clean air / air with a low level of sulfur dioxide to grow *[1 mark]*.

Page 48 — Food Chains and Food Webs
Q1 E.g. the number of hawks might increase because there will be more mice for them to eat *[1 mark]*. The amount of wheat might decrease because more will be eaten by the mice *[1 mark]*. The number of aphids might decrease because they would be competing with more mice for food *[1 mark]*. The number of humans might decrease because they would be competing with more mice for food *[1 mark]*.

Page 49 — Pyramids of Biomass and Number
Q1 B, because the bar for the producer is smaller than for the primary consumer *[1 mark]* and just one tree/large plant may feed many consumers *[1 mark]*.

Page 50 — Biomass Transfer
Q1 Any two from: e.g. respiration / egestion / not all of an organism is eaten *[1 mark for each correct answer, up to 2 marks]*
Q2 110 ÷ 995 × 100 = 11.1% *[1 mark]*

Page 51 — Making and Breaking Biological Molecules
Q1 a) simple sugars *[1 mark]*
b) amino acids *[1 mark]*

Page 52 — Testing for Biological Molecules
Q1 Proteins are present *[1 mark]*.

Page 53 — Cycles in Ecosystems
Q1 E.g. not as much CO_2 in the air is being used for photosynthesis *[1 mark]*. Microorganisms involved in the decomposition of the dead trees release CO_2 into the atmosphere through respiration *[1 mark]*.

Page 54 — More on Cycles in Ecosystems
Q1 a) By evaporation / transpiration *[1 mark]*
b) By providing them with fresh water *[1 mark]*.

Page 55 — Decomposition
Q1 Any two from: e.g. make sure that plenty of oxygen can get in to the waste. / Keep the waste in a warm place. / Make sure that the waste is moist but not too wet. *[1 mark for each correct answer, up to 2 marks]*

Page 57 — Respiration
Q1 glucose + oxygen → carbon dioxide + water *[1 mark for correct reactants, 1 mark for correct products.]*

Page 58 — More on Respiration
Q1 Ethanol and carbon dioxide *[1 mark]*.
Q2 E.g. aerobic respiration produces much more ATP than anaerobic respiration *[1 mark]*.

Page 59 — The Cell Cycle and Mitosis
Q1 The cell grows larger *[1 mark]*, increases the amount of its subcellular structures *[1 mark]* and duplicates its DNA *[1 mark]*.

Page 60 — Microscopy
Q1 They've allowed us to see the internal structures of cells in more detail *[1 mark]*, which has allowed scientists to develop explanations as to how the structures are related to their functions *[1 mark]*.

Page 61 — More Microscopy
Q1 actual size = measured size ÷ magnification
= 7 × 10⁻¹ mm (or 0.7 mm) ÷ 400 *[1 mark]*
= 0.00175 mm *[1 mark]*
(× 1000) = 1.75 µm *[1 mark]*

Page 62 — Sexual Reproduction and Meiosis
Q1 During fertilisation, a male gamete fuses with a female gamete to form a zygote/fertilised egg *[1 mark]*. Gametes need half the chromosome number so that the zygote/fertilised egg ends up with the full number of chromosomes, and not twice as many *[1 mark]*.

Page 63 — Stem Cells
Q1 The tips of plant shoots contain meristem tissue *[1 mark]*. Meristems produce unspecialised cells that are able to divide and form any cell type in the plant *[1 mark]*. This means the plant is able to produce all the different specialised cells it needs in order to grow into a new plant *[1 mark]*.

Page 64 — Plant Growth
Q1 a shoot *[1 mark]*

Page 65 — More on Plant Growth
Q1 E.g. stimulates seed germination *[1 mark]*, stimulates flowering/bolting *[1 mark]*.

Page 67 — Exchange of Materials
Q1 Surface area:
(1 × 1) × 2 = 2
(4 × 1) × 4 = 16
2 + 16 = 18 µm² *[1 mark]*
Volume:
1 × 1 × 4 = 4 µm³ *[1 mark]*
So the surface area to volume ratio is 18 : 4, which is 9 : 2 in its simplest form *[1 mark]*.
(In this question the ratio has been simplified down to the smallest whole numbers. It's not in the form n : 1 because then n would not be a whole number.)

Page 68 — Human Exchange Surfaces
Q1 E.g. they have a large surface area. / They have a moist lining for dissolving gases. / They have very thin walls. / They have a good blood supply. *[1 mark]*

Page 69 — The Circulatory System
Q1 the right ventricle *[1 mark]*

Page 70 — Blood Vessels
Q1 They have a big lumen to help the blood flow despite the low pressure *[1 mark]* and they have valves to keep the blood flowing in the right direction *[1 mark]*.
Q2 E.g. networks of capillaries carry blood to every cell in the body to exchange substances with them *[1 mark]*. They have permeable walls, so that substances can easily diffuse in and out of them *[1 mark]*. Their walls are only one cell thick, which increases the rate of diffusion *[1 mark]*.

Page 71 — Blood
Q1 Haemoglobin *[1 mark]*.
Q2 Any three from: e.g. Red blood cells have a large surface area to volume ratio for absorbing oxygen / They don't have a nucleus, which allows more room for carrying oxygen / They contain haemoglobin, which can combine with oxygen in the lungs and release it in body tissues / They're small and flexible so they can easily pass through tiny capillaries. *[3 marks — 1 mark for each correct answer]*

Page 72 — The Nervous System
Q1 brain *[1 mark]*, spinal cord *[1 mark]*

Page 73 — The Brain
Q1 Cerebellum *[1 mark]*.

Page 74 — Hormones and Negative Feedback
Q1 Endocrine glands secrete hormones *[1 mark]*. These act as chemical messengers *[1 mark]* and travel in the bloodstream *[1 mark]* to effectors *[1 mark]*. These have receptors so they can respond to the hormone *[1 mark]*.

Page 75 — Hormones in Reproduction
Q1 LH stimulates the release of an egg/ovulation *[1 mark]*. It also stimulates the remains of the follicle to secrete progesterone *[1 mark]*.

Page 76 — Hormones for Fertility and Contraception
Q1 The hormones FSH and LH *[1 mark]* can be injected by women with naturally low FSH levels *[1 mark]* to stimulate ovulation *[1 mark]*.

Page 77 — More on Contraception
Q1 E.g. oral contraceptives can have unpleasant side-effects *[1 mark]*. / She might find it difficult to remember to take a pill every day *[1 mark]*.
Q2 Any two from: e.g. IUDs are more effective. / IUDs are longer acting. / There's less chance of IUDs not working as they are intended. *[1 mark for each correct answer, up to 2 marks]*

Page 78 — Homeostasis
Q1 Less blood flows near the surface of the skin *[1 mark]* because blood vessels near the surface constrict (vasoconstriction) *[1 mark]*. This means less energy is transferred to the surroundings, which helps keep the person warm *[1 mark]*.

Page 79 — More on Homeostasis
Q1 Receptors in the skin/hypothalamus detect when the body temperature is to high or too low *[1 mark]*. The hypothalamus then processes the information and communicates via the nervous system to effectors *[1 mark]*. The effectors respond to counteract the body temperature, bringing it back to normal *[1 mark]*.

Page 80 — Controlling Water Content
Q1 The cell may burst/lysis may occur *[1 mark]* as there will be a net movement of water into the cell by osmosis *[1 mark]*.

Page 81 — More on Controlling Water Content
Q1 ADH helps to control the blood water content *[1 mark]* as it increases the permeability of the kidney tubules *[1 mark]*, which increases the amount of water reabsorbed back into the blood *[1 mark]*.

Answers

Q2 When it's hot, more sweat may be produced *[1 mark]*. Sweat causes water to be lost from the body *[1 mark]*. When the brain detects the fall in the water content of the blood, it triggers feelings of thirst *[1 mark]*.

Page 82 — Controlling Blood Sugar Level
Q1 In type 1 diabetes, the person doesn't produce insulin *[1 mark]*, whereas in type 2 diabetes, the person still produces insulin but they are resistant to it/don't respond properly to it *[1 mark]* or don't produce enough of it *[1 mark]*.

Page 83 — The Eye
Q1 The ciliary muscles contract *[1 mark]*, which slackens the suspensory ligaments *[1 mark]*. The lens becomes fat/more curved *[1 mark]*. This increases the amount by which it refracts light, so the image is focused on the retina *[1 mark]*.

Page 84 — Correcting Vision Defects
Q1 By replacing the faulty/cloudy lens with an artificial one made of clear plastic *[1 mark]*.
Q2 The lens is the wrong shape / refracts the light too much, or the eyeball is too long *[1 mark]*. So light rays do not converge on the retina *[1 mark]* and images of distant objects are brought into focus in front of the retina *[1 mark]*.

Page 86 — Natural Selection and Evolution
Q1 Some of the musk oxen may have had a genetic variant/allele which gave them thicker fur *[1 mark]*. These oxen would have been more likely to survive and reproduce *[1 mark]* and so pass on the genetic variant/allele for thicker fur *[1 mark]*. This process of natural selection may have continued over many generations, until all the musk oxen had thick fur *[1 mark]*.

Page 87 — Evidence for Evolution
Q1 by mutations *[1 mark]*
Q2 Fossils can show what organisms that lived a long time ago looked like *[1 mark]*. Arranging them in chronological/date order shows how organisms gradually changed/developed *[1 mark]*.

Page 88 — Selective Breeding
Q1 He should choose the bean plants that are best at surviving the drought *[1 mark]* and breed them with each other *[1 mark]*. He should then continue this process over several generations *[1 mark]*.

Page 89 — Darwin and Wallace
Q1 Any two from: e.g. the similarities and differences between fossils and living organisms *[1 mark]*. / The similarities and differences between organisms living on different islands *[1 mark]*. / The way in which selective breeding can produce new varieties of an organism *[1 mark]*.

Page 90 — Asexual and Sexual Reproduction
Q1 E.g. asexual reproduction produces genetically identical organisms *[1 mark]*. This means that if environmental conditions change, making it difficult for the strawberry plant to survive, the whole population of strawberry plants could be affected *[1 mark]*.

Page 91 — Classification
Q1 E.g. organisms may be very similar physically but have many genetic differences / belong to different species *[1 mark]*.

Page 92 — Biodiversity
Q1 E.g. chemicals used in agriculture may pollute water sources *[1 mark]*, affecting organisms which rely on the water for survival *[1 mark]*.

Page 93 — More on Biodiversity
Q1 E.g. captive breeding programmes in zoos can be used to increase the number of Siberian tigers *[1 mark]*. Some of these individuals can then be released into the wild *[1 mark]*.

Page 94 — Biodiversity and The Distribution of Organisms
Q1 E.g. a change in the availability of water *[1 mark]*, a change in atmospheric gases *[1 mark]*.

Page 95 — Maintaining Biodiversity
Q1 E.g. undiscovered plant species may contain new medicinal chemicals *[1 mark]*. If these plants are allowed to become extinct we could miss out on valuable medicines *[1 mark]*.

Page 96 — Human Food Security
Q1 E.g. a pathogen such as a bacterium, fungus or virus could result in the loss of crops *[1 mark]* and could lead to widespread famine reducing the level of food security *[1 mark]*.

Index

Index

Index